Disposal and Decontamination of Pesticides

Disposal and Decontamination of Pesticides

Maurice V. Kennedy, EDITOR

Mississippi State University

A symposium sponsored by

the Division of Pesticide

Chemistry at the 174th

Meeting of the American

Chemical Society, Chicago,

Illinois, August 29–

September 2, 1977.

ACS SYMPOSIUM SERIES **73**

AMERICAN CHEMICAL SOCIETY

WASHINGTON, D. C.   1978

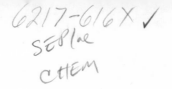

Library of Congress CIP Data

Main entry under title:
Disposal and decontamination of pesticides.
  (ACS symposium; no. 73)

  Includes index and bibliographical references.

  1. Pesticides—Environmental aspects—Congresses.
  I. Kennedy, Maurice V., 1925–   . II. American
Chemical Society. Division of Pesticide Chemistry.
III. American Chemical Society. IV. Series: American
Chemical Society. ACS symposium series; no. 73.

TD196.P38D57   668'.65   78–8645
ISBN 0–8412–0443–0   ACSMC8 73 1–158

ACS Symposium Series

Robert F. Gould, *Editor*

FOREWORD

The ACS SYMPOSIUM SERIES was founded in 1974 to provide a medium for publishing symposia quickly in book form. The format of the SERIES parallels that of the continuing ADVANCES IN CHEMISTRY SERIES except that in order to save time the papers are not typeset but are reproduced as they are submitted by the authors in camera-ready form. As a further means of saving time, the papers are not edited or reviewed except by the symposium chairman, who becomes editor of the book. Papers published in the ACS SYMPOSIUM SERIES are original contributions not published elsewhere in whole or major part and include reports of research as well as reviews since symposia may embrace both types of presentation.

CONTENTS

PREFACE

The decontamination and disposal of waste pesticides is one of the major problems facing the leaders in modern agriculture today. It poses many complex problems involving other segments of society as well. This has become apparent in recent years by reports of varying amounts of pesticide chemicals widely distributed in unwanted areas owing to either misuse or lack of information relative to disposal.

All of these chemicals are not confined to direct agricultural use. Many are by-products or waste compounds resulting from synthesis or formulation of these products. Occasionally an industrial accident will release hazardous chemicals included in this general classification. However, the frequency of this occurring is small and it could not be considered to be very important.

One of the main reasons that decontamination and disposal of these hazardous waste chemicals is such a complex problem involves the wide range of chemical compounds which are used as pesticides. For example, two classes of compounds—the organochlorines and the organophosphates —vary greatly in their response to many of the methods used for decontamination, and these are only two of the classes of compounds used as pesticides.

This wide range of chemicals makes research extremely difficult, if not impossible, for producing a single method for pesticide disposal that applies universally. Therefore, several methods for decontamination and disposal of these unwanted chemicals may be required to solve this problem.

The aim of this volume is to present several methods that have either been successful or show a great deal of promise in the destruction of these compounds. These research reports cover a wide range of methods and should be highly applicable to the major classes of pesticide chemicals in use today.

Appreciation is expressed to all of the authors of this publication for the quality of research reported herein. It is hoped that these investigations will serve as a basis for further research and that they eventually will lead to satisfactory solutions for all of these problems.

Mississippi State University   MAURICE V. KENNEDY
Mississippi State, Mississippi
February, 1978

Conquering the Monster—The Photochemical Destruction of Chlorodioxins

D. G. CROSBY

Department of Environmental Toxicology, University of California, Davis, CA 95616

2,3,7,8-Tetrachlorodibenzo-p-dioxin (TCDD) has become recognized as probably the most poisonous of all synthetic chemicals. In addition to having a high acute toxicity, it is mutagenic, embryotoxic, and causes skin disorders at very low exposure levels (1). It also has been considered to be very persistent (2) and to bioconcentrate in animals. No wonder that a 1976 newspaper article referred to it as "the monsterous chemical" and that its detectable presence in Vietnam War defoliants, commercial herbicides, and elsewhere in the environment has caused so much apprehension and controversy.

The use of products which could contain chlorinated dibenzo-p-dioxins has been remarkably widespread (3). Pesticides such as 2,4,5-T, chlorophenols used for slime- and algae-control, and the common bactericide hexachlorophene--in fact, any chemical made from 2,4,5-trichlorophenol--might contain traces of TCDD. Commercial pentachlorophenol (PCP), used primarily as a preservative and insecticide, contains hexa-, hepta-, and octachlorodioxins which can be reduced biologically to less-chlorinated homologs; for example "chick-edema" disease has been traced to dioxins formed in PCP-treated hides from which a poultry-feed supplement was derived (4). The manufacture of chlorophenols, especially, has led on occasion to severe toxicological problems such as those encountered in a 1976 accident at Seveso, Italy.

Earlier work indicated that pure TCDD was almost inert toward attack by microorganisms, other biological breakdown, and environmental forces (2). This is not strictly true; under certain conditions, it is very unstable to ultraviolet (UV) light (5). The purpose of the present paper is to define the photochemical criteria for that instability, describe laboratory experiments concerned with it, and indicate how it might be applied for the intentional destruction of "the monstrous chemical" and its relatives.

Background Photochemistry

The photochemical replacement of halogen atoms on aromatic rings by hydrogen has been known for some time. For example, the irradiation of pentachlorophenol in hexane with UV light produced tetrachlorophenols, pentachloronitrobenzene (PCNB) was reduced to tetrachloronitrobenzenes and pentachlorobenzene, and polychlorobenzenes were further dechlorinated (6) (Fig. 1). However, thin films of the pure compounds were not appreciably affected; some donor of hydrogen atoms also was necessary for the reaction. Organic solvents serve this purpose admirably, although photoreduction experiments with chlorobenzoic acids revealed that the chemical nature of that solvent could strongly influence the rate of reaction (7).

Although photonucleophilic displacement reactions of aromatic halides have been shown to be commonplace in aqueous solution (8), most evidence for the mechanism of reductive dechlorination in organic solvents supports an initial homolysis of the relatively weak C-Cl bond followed by abstraction of the hydrogen atom from solvent by the resulting phenyl radical (Fig. 2). For example, when the solvent is benzene, phenylation rather than hydrogenation often predominates (9), and the above-mentioned photoreduction of PCNB in hexane also produced the three isomeric chlorohexanes by transfer of chlorine atoms (6). This mechanistic problem is by no means solved, but Nordblom and Miller (7) confirmed that the chlorine-replacing hydrogen indeed is derived by breaking C-H bonds of the solvent.

As might be expected, this reductive dechlorination of polyhalogenated compounds takes place stepwise (Fig. 3). UV irradiation of tetrachlorobiphenyls in organic solvents produced corresponding tri-, di-, and monochlorobiphenyls, but the monochloro compound proved to be essentially stable toward further reaction due to negligible absorption of the light energy provided (10). The same phenomenon has been observed in the photoreduction of chlorinated benzonitriles (11); the rate of the primary homolytic (bond-breaking) process in the halide is dependent upon the degree of light absorption as measured by the compound's molar extinction coefficient, ε. Consequently, the relationship of the incident light to the UV absorption spectrum of the halide as well as to that of any other strongly-absorbing compound present becomes extremely important. It is apparent that three conditions must exist in order for photoreduction of chlorinated aromatic compounds to take place: a hydrogen-donating solvent must be present, UV light of appropriate wavelength must impinge on the solution, and that light must be absorbed.

The energy available in natural sunlight limits the photoreduction of many chemicals in the environment. Sunlight intensity drops off abruptly below about 310 nm (Fig. 4) and becomes negligible below about 290 nm. Consequently, it is not surprising that 3,3',4,4'-tetrachlorobiphenyl (ε = 6740 at 290 nm) is readily

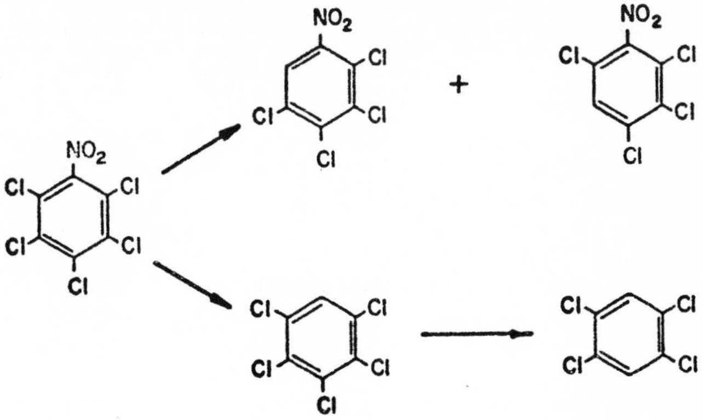

Figure 1.   Photodecomposition products from PCNB in hexane

ArCl $\xrightarrow{\ hv\ }$ Ar· + Cl·   Primary
                                                Process

Ar· + C_6H_{14} $\longrightarrow$ ArH + C_6H_{13}·
                                                Reactions
Cl· + C_6H_{13}· $\longrightarrow$ $C_6H_{13}Cl$

Ar· + Ar· $\longrightarrow$ Ar_2
                                                Side-
C_6H_{13}· + C_6H_{13}· $\longrightarrow$ $C_{12}H_{26}$ Reactions

Etc.

Figure 2.   *Proposed mechanism of photochemical reduction of aromatic halides in an organic solvent (e.g., hexane)*

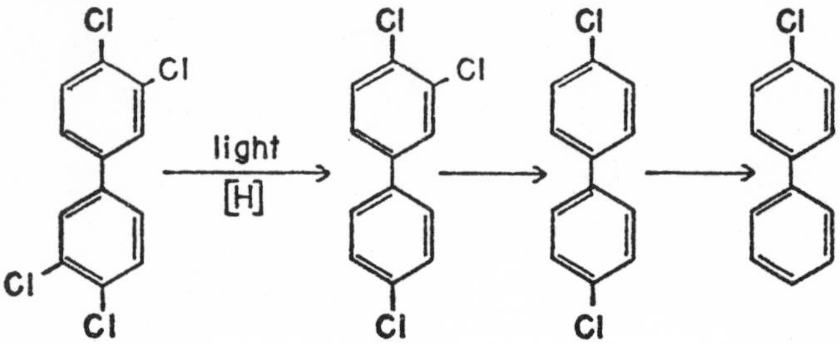

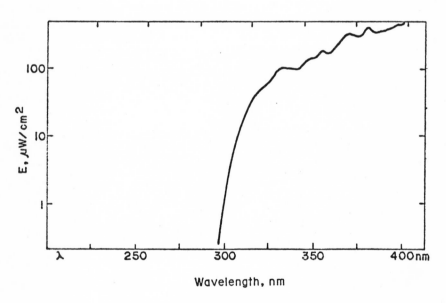

Figure 3.   Stepwise photoreduction of 3,3',4,4'-tetrachlorobiphenyl
in organic solvents

Figure 4.   Spectral energy distribution of sunlight

reduced at sunlight wavelengths ($\underline{7},\underline{10}$), while 4-chlorobiphenyl is relatively stable (ε = 10 at 310 $\overline{\text{nm}}$); only substances which absorb UV light above 290 nm can be expected to react.

Chlorodioxins

Like other chlorinated aromatic compounds, chlorodioxins are reductively dechlorinated when their solutions in organic solvents are irradiated with appropriate wavelengths of UV light ($\underline{12}$). Exposure of a dilute methanol solution of TCDD (λ_{max} 306 nm, ε = 6000) to light from a fluorescent UV lamp caused rapid degradation (Fig. 5); the initial product, 2,3,7-trichlorodibenzo-p-dioxin, which exhibits a very similar absorption spectrum but has only about half the molar extinction (λ_{max} 304 nm, ε = 3500), slowly accumulated and then itself disappeared. 1,2,3,4,6,7,8,9-Octa-chlorodibenzo-p-dioxin (OCDD), with λ_{max} 318 nm and ε 4000, reacted even more slowly (Fig. 6). Less-chlorinated photoreduc-tion products were readily detected and identified by gas chroma-tography and mass spectrometry in each instance.

Pure, crystalline TCDD was stable to sunlight wavelengths when applied as thin films to glass ($\underline{5}$) or leaves ($\underline{12}$) or suspend-ed in water ($\underline{3}$). Apparently, the crystalline state prohibits TCDD molecules from losing significant chlorine or from abstracting hydrogen atoms from each other. However, when dissolved in methanol ($\underline{5}$), diesel oil ($\underline{13}$), or liquid phenoxy ester ($\underline{13}$), photoreduction was complete after a few hours' exposure to outdoor sunlight. Again, trichloro-and dichloro-homologs were detected during photolysis, but they in turn eventually were dechlorinated to nontoxic dibenzo-p-dioxin which itself underwent further photodegradation ($\underline{3}$). This suggests that TCDD may decompose under many practical application conditions and that it even could be intentionally destroyed as long as the three photochemical cri-teria cited above were satisfied.

Practical Applications

Continuing concern has been expressed over the presence of small but detectable levels of TCDD in commercial herbicide formu-lations. Typically, such formulations are composed of roughly equal amounts of liquid esters of 2,4-D (2,4-dichlorophenoxyacetic acid) and 2,4,5-T (2,4,5-trichlorophenoxyacetic acid), usually dissolved in oil or emulsified in water (Table I). The fear is that the contained dioxin--currently less than 0.1 ppm but origin-ally as much as 100 times more than that--might persist and bio-concentrate following field application of herbicides.

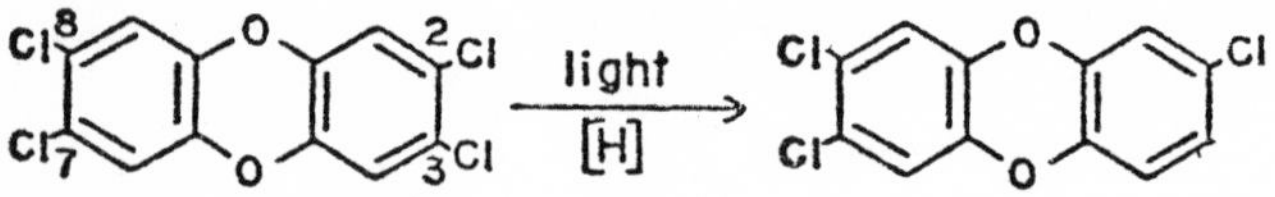

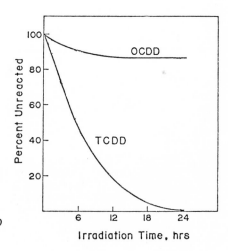

Figure 5.   Stepwise photoreduction of TCDD

Figure 6.   Photoreduction rates of TCDD
and OCDD in methanol (5 mg/L)

Table I. Composition of Herbicide Sprays

Esteron[R] Brush-killer	Lbs/Acre
Water	100
2,4-D propylene glycol ether esters	1.52
2,4,5-T propylene glycol ether esters	1.45[a]
Organic solvent and emulsifier	1.26
Agent Orange	
2,4-D n-butyl ester	15.0
2,4,5-T n-butyl ester	16.8[b]
Alcohols, acids, etc.	0.6

[a]Equivalent to 1 lb/acre 2,4,5-T (<45 µg/acre TCDD).

[b]Equivalent to 13.8 lbs/acre 2,4,5-T (~20 mg/acre TCDD);
see Ref. 22.

The herbicide esters should serve adequately as H-donors,
TCDD absorbs light within the wavelength range of sunlight, and
the thin films of applied chemicals do not completely mask this UV
absorption (14). Consequently, when herbicide was applied to a
leaf surface (13), the breakdown of TCDD was found to be rapid
upon exposure to sunlight (Fig. 7). Photochemical breakdown also
occurred on the surface of soil, although once sufficient herbicide had been applied so that it penetrated, the subsurface portion no longer was exposed to light and the degradation presumably
ceased. Because much of the UV light reaching the earth's surface
comes from open sky (15), exposure to direct sunlight was not
required, but breakdown would be expected to be slower in the
shade.

Despite recent furor over the continued use of 2,4,5-T in
Western forests, no actual measurements of dioxin dissipation from
herbicide-treated forest appear to have been reported. However,
the breakdown observed upon application to broadleaved plants (13)
might be expected to take place in other locations as well, provided that the three criteria for photoreduction were met.
Getzendaner and coworkers indeed have shown (16) that TCDD was
lost smoothly from 2,4,5-T treated range grass, the half-life
being roughly 4 days. Evidently, the photochemical destruction of
TCDD takes place under field conditions.

Analysis of TCDD residues in the presence of the large excess
of phenoxy esters proved troublesome. The procedure was greatly
simplified by alkaline hydrolysis of the esters, removal of the
neutral dioxin into inert solvent (such as benzene), concentration
of the extract, and gas chromatography of the dioxins with either
an electron-capture or mass spectrometer detector (13). This
principle of herbicide hydrolysis followed by extraction of dioxin
from the alkaline hydrolyzate was applied by the Velsicol Chemical

Corporation of Chicago to a process aimed at practical utilization of the millions of gallons of leftover Agent Orange (mixed butyl esters of 2,4-D and 2,4,5-T) stored by the U.S. Air Force. Velsicol's method utilized the n-butyl alcohol resulting from the hydrolysis of the phenoxy acid butyl esters as part of the extraction solvent; the dioxin-containing organic extract was continuously subjected to UV irradiation in a separate reactor to produce a harmless residue which could be safely incinerated, while the dioxin-free mixture of 2,4-D and 2,4,5-T salts remaining in the aqueous layer could be reprocessed and fortified to provide a useful registered herbicide. The photochemical destruction of TCDD apparently is applicable to appropriate industrial processing.

The release of TCDD has not always been under such close control; in fact, several industrial accidents have resulted in human illness and severe damage to property. On July 10, 1976, an overheated still at a trichlorophenol plant in Seveso, Italy, released a cloud of sodium trichlorophenate which contained thermally-generated TCDD. The particles settled out over several hundred acres of primarily agricultural grassland and trees as well as a number of dwellings. In the most highly contaminated area, grass levels reached many micrograms per square meter ($\mu g/m^2$), while the leaves of nearby trees contained as much as 2.5 milligrams of TCDD per kilogram of wet weight. Human contact with levels exceeding about 0.5 $\mu g/m^2$ is considered extremely dangerous.

Extensive analytical work by both the Italian Government and the owner of the factory (Givaudan Corporation) showed that the TCDD residues were dissipating very slowly; although the sunlight was adequate and the TCDD absorption appropriate, effective contact with photochemical H-donors was minimal. Application of a number of harmless solvents to artificially provide the needed hydrogen was considered but was rejected by a people who felt that they already had been sprayed with enough chemicals. Finally, Givaudan chemists offered an acceptable hydrogen donor--olive oil.

The locally-purchased oil was applied experimentally by sprayer to a highly contaminated area of glassland as a 40% aqueous emulsion (400 l/ha) or 80% solution in cyclohexanone (350 l/ha) to produce a practically continuous film on vegetation and other surfaces (17). As seen in Table II, reduction of the residue levels in the treated plots was rapid while controls remained virtually unchanged, although a period of rain washed a large proportion of the control TCDD onto the soil. Despite considerable variability when the analytical values were plotted against time, a plot against accumulated (integrated) ultraviolet energy (Fig. 8) provided a clear demonstration of photochemical decomposition which, in the case of the olive oil solution, resulted in the destruction of almost 90% of the TCDD within 9 days. In view of this, it was hoped that dioxin could be reduced to a tolerable level over the entire area-at least enough to permit safe harvest-

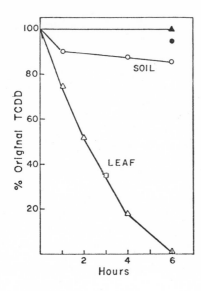

Figure 7. *Photoreduction rates of TCDD on leaves and soil treated with Agent Orange. Closed symbols denote dark controls.*

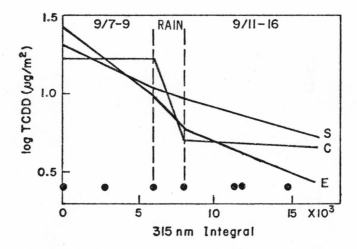

Figure 8. *Photodecomposition rates of TCDD on grass after treatment with olive oil emulsion (E) or olive oil solution in cyclohexanone (S) compared with an untreated control (C). Based upon data of Homberger et al. (17) from experiments at Seveso, Italy, September 7–16, 1976. Circles show sampling times; UV integral in arbitrary energy units.*

ing of the foliage with TCDD still in place--and that the people
of Seveso could return to their homes before winter.

Table II. TCDD on Grass
$(\mu g/m^2)^a$

Day	Olive Oil Emulsion	Olive Oil Solution	Control
0	26.2	19.5	16.4
1	16.9	18.8	18.5
2	9.6	10.7	16.4
3	Rain		
4	8.3	7.6	4.7
8	6.0	4.0	7.1
9	5.2	2.3	3.3

[a]Homberger et al., 1976.

Conclusions

Although the chemical mechanism which underlies TCDD photoreduction still may be obscure, the application of the principle
now seems clear enough. For reaction of halogenated aromatic
compounds (and perhaps nitro compounds, nitriles, and some others)
to occur, three factors are required: availability of UV light;
absorption of the light by the chemical; and the proximity of a
hydrogen-donating solvent.

Although intensity varies from location to location, the
energy required for photoreduction usually is present. The UV
portion of sunlight offers sufficient quantum energy to dissociate
both aromatic C-Cl bonds (about 97 kcal/Einstein, corresponding to
294 nm) and aliphatic C-H bonds (about 94 kcal/Einstein, or 303
nm) (18). A major part of this light reaches earth by reflection
and dispersion from open sky rather than from direct sunlight
(15)--in the long summer days of the Northern Hemisphere, the time
when most pesticides are applied, Barrow, Alaska, receives at
least as much total sunlight energy as Miami, Florida (18). The
UV radiation readily penetrates water (19), and recent estimates
have shown that a significant proportion penetrates the leaf
canopy of a forest or orchard (20).

Many aromatic compounds, including the dioxins, absorb appreciable energy within the UV portion of the solar spectrum (above
290 nm). Although that energy can be lost as heat, fluorescence,
or nonreactive impact with other molecules, the accumulating
evidence shows that reactions with environmental reagents are
prevalent (21). For photoreductions, the hydrogen-donating solvent could be a pesticide or formulating agent, leaf waxes, the
natural organic film which covers most natural water, or even

inadvertent and otherwise undesirable pollutants such as spilled oil. Although photoreduction is hardly a panacea, it obviously holds promise for the natural deactivation of residual chemicals, the destruction of toxic wastes from manufacturing, and even the intentional decontamination of polluted environments.

In view of this, what utilization has been made of the practical applications of photochemical reduction demonstrated above? None. Rather than attempt to determine whether or not TCDD actually was present in herbicide formulations applied to Western forests, for example, or to measure its dissipation in a forest environment, considerable effort has been expanded toward trying to demonstrate its presence in local human milk at or below the limit of analytical realiability; the fear and controversy continue. Despite presentation of a safe, practical process for the economical recovery of the herbicides in Agent Orange, the obviously impractical removal of TCDD by an adsorption process was tried, abandoned, and the decision finally was made by the U.S. Air Force to burn the material at sea. The Italian government hesitated too long to reduce TCDD levels on foliage, and winter rains and leaf fall carried most of the chemical into the soil; they now are considering construction of what may be one of the world's largest kilns in which to "burn" soil and organic matter, turning the Seveso agricultural area into a wasteland. In each instance, there is evidence that decision-makers failed to comprehend the firm scientific principles upon which the application was based.

Distressing as they may be, these disappointments underscore several important conclusions:
- --- Laboratory investigations in environmental chemistry must more closely simulate the physical and chemical microenvironment in which toxic chemicals actually exist if valid conclusions about transformations (and movement) are to be drawn;
- --- Formulating agents play a more important part in the environmental fate of pesticides than previously has been supposed;
- --- TCDD and related chlorodioxins, no matter how toxic and dangerous, are only chemicals and obey known physical and chemical principles.
- --- Chemists must become much more proficient and forceful in conveying these principles to news media, the public, and society's leaders if maximum utilization is to be achieved in applying chemistry for mankind's benefit.

Literature Cited

1. Schwetz, B.A., J.M. Morris, G.L. Sparschu, V.K. Rowe, and P.J. Gehring, Adv. in Chem. Ser. 120, 55 (1973).
2. Kearney, P.C., A.R. Isensee, C.S. Helling, E.A. Woolson, and J.R. Plimmer, Adv. in Chem. Ser. 120, 105 (1973).

3. Plimmer, J.R., U.I. Klingebiel, D.G. Crosby, and A.S. Wong, Adv. in Chem. Series 120, 44 (1973).
4. Higginbotham, J.R., A. Huang, D. Firestone, J. Verrett, J. Ress, and A.D. Campbell, Nature 220, 702 (1968).
5. Crosby, D.G., A.S. Wong, J.R. Plimmer, and U.I. Klingebiel, Science 173, 748 (1971).
6. Crosby, D.G., and N. Hamadmad, J. Agr. Food Chem. 19, 1171 (1971).
7. Nordblom, G.D., and L.L. Miller, J. Agr. Food Chem. 22, 57 (1974).
8. Crosby, D.G., K.W. Moilanen, M. Nakagawa, and A.S. Wong, in "Environmental Toxicology of Pesticides" (F. Matsumura, G.M. Boush, and T. Misato, eds.), Academic Press, New York, 1973, p. 423.
9. Plimmer, J.R., and B.E. Hummer, Abstr. Weed Sci. Soc. Amer., 1968, 20.
10. Ruzo, L.O., M.J. Zabik, and R.D. Schuetz, J. Agr. Food Chem. 22, 199 (1974).
11. Plimmer, J.R., Residue Reviews 33, 47 (1970).
12. Isensee, A.R., and G.E. Jones, J. Agr. Food Chem. 19, 1210 (1971).
13. Crosby, D.G., and A.S. Wong, Science 195, 1337 (1977).
14. Crosby, D.G., K.W. Moilanen, and A.S. Wong, Environ. Health Perspectives 5, 259 (1973).
15. Koller, L.R., "Ultraviolet Radiation," 2nd ed., Wiley, New York, 1965.
16. Getzendaner, M.E, Ag-Organics Department, Dow Chemical USA, Midland, Mich. Personal Communication.
17. Homberger, E., N. Neuner, F. Schenker, and H.K. Wipf, Workshop on 2,3,7,8-Tetrachlorodibenzo-p-dioxin (TCDD), University of Milan, October 23/24, 1976.
18. Crosby, D.G., Herbicide Photodecomposition, in "Herbicides: Chemistry, Degradation, and Mode of Action" (P.C. Kearney and D.D. Kaufman, eds.), Vol. 2, Marcel Dekker, New York, 1976, p. 835.
19. Zepp, R.G., and D.M. Cline, Environ. Sci. Technol. 11, 359 (1977).
20. Allen, L.H., H.W. Gausman, and W.A. Allen, J. Environ. Qual. 4, 285 (1975).
21. Crosby, D.G., ACS Sympos. Ser. 37, 93 (1977).
22. National Research Council, "The effects of herbicides in South Vietnam," National Academy of Sciences, Washington, D.C., 1974.

MARCH 23, 1978

Approaches to Decontamination or Disposal of Pesticides: Photodecomposition

JACK R. PLIMMER

Organic Chemical Synthesis Laboratory, Federal Research, Science, and
Education Administration, USDA, Beltsville, MD 20705

The guidelines for the disposal of small quantities of unused pesticides issued by the Environmental Protection Agency in
1975 make it clear that there is still a great need for satisfactory disposal techniques for a variety of pesticides. Specifically the guidelines state "safe disposal procedures are most
urgently needed for those pesticides that do not have acceptable
disposal procedures at present and are either: (a) extremely
dangerous to man and wildlife because of their high toxicity;
(b) not, or only slowly degraded to nontoxic products in the
environment; or (c) produced in the largest quantities. Pesticides in these categories include the organomercury and organo-
arsenic compounds, thallium sulfate, diazinon, methyl parathion,
parathion, phorate, maneb, alachlor, CDAA, propachlor, atrazine,
DDT, heptachlor, toxaphene, lindane, chloramben, 2,4-D, 2,4,5-T,
aldrin, chlordane, endrin, pentachlorophenol and 2,4,6-trichloro-
phenol" (1).

Photochemical destruction of organic material has not
achieved the status of a technological process that is applicable
on a large scale; indeed, its potential for detoxication of
wastes or rendering them more susceptible to microbial degradation has been little explored. There is an important need to
develop more data on rates and efficiencies of photochemical
reactions. Without this basic data, there is little point in
discussing the question of installation design and calculation
of operating costs. In this discussion I would like to outline
some limiting factors and indicate areas where progress is de-
sirable.

Microbial action and the effect of sunlight are two major
factors responsible for transformation of pesticides in the
environment. If the pesticide is applied as a spray, a substantial proportion of the applied material may not reach the
target site and an appreciable amount may be lost by volatilization. Pesticides vaporizing from surfaces or during spray
application may be transformed by photolysis in the vapor phase;
similarly pesticides in water or present on environmental

surfaces may be altered chemically by solar radiation. If small
quantities of pesticides are exposed to the prolonged action of
air, sunlight and microbial degradation, it is to be anticipated
that in most cases there will be rapid breakdown to simpler
molecules.

The problems involved in intentional decontamination and
disposal of concentrated pesticide wastes are somewhat different.
Incineration appears to have greatest practical potential as a
disposal technique when substantial quantities of surplus
combustible materials are concentrated at a single location. It
provides a complete solution to many problems of chemical disposal, but it is important that the conditions required for the
combustion of each chemical be previously determined and that the
flue gases be efficiently cleaned and monitored to ensure that
no toxic materials are released (2). Such conditions demand
equipment that is costly to install and operate.

If large volumes of materials are to be handled, other
options may be preferable. Soil disposal offers a feasible and
economically attractive alternative, but suitable sites are
limited and the correct choice of site is of critical importance
(3). Dilute aqueous wastes may be applied to suitably constructed soil disposal areas or purified by passage through percolation
beds and holding tanks. Soil disposal relies on microbial action
to transform pesticides into simple innocuous molecules. This
process, involving conversion of complex molecules to carbon
dioxide, water, chloride ion etc., is generally referred to as
"mineralization".

We can also add chemical treatment and irradiation to the
processes of microbial action and incineration as ways to reduce
the hazards of surplus pesticides. Chemical treatment of organic
compounds may include reactions such as conversion to carbon
tetrachloride by the process of chlorinolysis, which implies
reaction with gaseous chlorine under vigorous conditions. Treatment with other reagents such as sodium hydroxide may be used;
for example, a strong base rapidly increases the rate of
hydrolysis of organophosphorus pesticides such as parathion.
Thus toxicity may be substantially reduced. A variety of
chemical treatments have been investigated. Kennedy et al. (4)
found that several pesticides could be effectively degraded by
dissolving metal reduction (sodium in liquid ammonia).

Organochlorine compounds present a particular problem. The
EPA guidelines state that "the only acceptable disposal procedure
for these pesticides is incineration. However, in most cases,
complex incineration equipment is required in order to assure
that sufficiently high temperatures are developed, and to prevent
atmospheric contamination by combustion products. Furthermore,
incineration is practical only on a very large scale and is un-
suited to the small batch operations which characterize most
pesticide disposal situations.

"We recommend that a study be made of other techniques.....

In particular, we recommend that a study be made of a disposal procedure which employs both hydrolysis and oxidation" (1).

In such cases, I suggest that the possibility of using irradiation followed by microbial degradation should also be examined as an alternative method to reduce the hazard of dilute aqueous wastes. Aqueous systems containing parts per million or less of chlorinated compounds or other toxic organic wastes may be irradiated to reduce their toxicity and also to reduce their "recalcitrance". If some parts of the molecules can be modified in this way, they may be rendered more susceptible to degradation by microorganisms. For example, a reduction in the number of chlorine atoms attached to an aromatic ring will generally increase the rate of decomposition by microorganisms. The breakdown of (2,4-dichlorophenoxy)acetic acid by soil microorganisms is much more rapid than that of (2,4,5-trichlorophenoxy)acetic acid. Similarly polychlorinated biphenyls containing few halogen substituents are more readily degraded than the more highly substituted molecules (5).

Photolysis as a method for the intentional destruction of pesticides would appear to have great potential. Sunlight as a source of radiant energy is freely available, and solar radiation is a potent agent for the destruction of many man-made chemicals in the environment. In fact, it is very difficult to synthesize organic chemicals that can resist the action of sun and air for long periods. Water is purified by the action of air and sunlight. Many toxic chemicals, such as the chlorodioxins, may be decomposed by ultraviolet radiation (6,7).

Most pesticides on ultraviolet irradiation ultimately afford products that are much less toxic or hazardous to the environment than the original material. It may be possible to take practical advantage of this fact if we are willing to examine the requirements and limitations of photochemical reactions.

Questions that must be considered include the following: 1) How rapidly do photochemical reactions occur and what energy input is necessary? 2) What products are to be anticipated and how are they affected by the physical state of the reactants?

How Rapidly do Photochemical Reactions Occur and What are Their Energy Requirements?

Most organic compounds can be decomposed by thermal energy, a process that usually takes place rapidly. How useful is ultraviolet irradiation, if we wish to achieve a similar effect?

First, the rupture of a chemical bond requires a definite amount of energy. Because the dissociation of a carbon-carbon bond requires an input of about 100 kilocalories per mole, we must use light possessing at least that amount of energy. The energy of electromagnetic radiation is inversely proportional to its wavelength so the source must provide a satisfactory output of energy at low wavelengths. A frequently used source for

photochemical reactions is the medium pressure mercury arc, with
maximum energy distribution around 254 nm. This source must be
housed in quartz to permit the passage of low wavelengths.

Secondly, the rate of photolysis depends on several factors.
Direct photolysis of an organic compound in solution requires that
light must be absorbed for reaction to occur. Light energy is
measured in quanta. The number of light quanta absorbed by the
reactant divided into the number of molecules of photolysis product formed measures the efficiency, or 'quantum yield', of
the process. However, the quantum yield of a photochemical
reaction does not provide a good indication of the reaction rate
because it is only one factor in determining the rate, which also
depends on the rate of absorption of light by the system and the
fraction of absorbed light that produces the reactive state (8).

Therefore the source of light must not only possess sufficient energy in terms of wavelength distribution, it must also
supply sufficient intensity in terms of radiant energy output
over unit time.

Absorption of light by the molecule is defined at any wavelength by the shape of its absorption curve. Benzenoid compounds
generally absorb light weakly around 300 nm, which corresponds
to the region of the solar spectrum providing most energy.
Cyclodiene insecticides such as aldrin or dieldrin do not absorb
light except at wavelengths below 250 nm. Such radiation requires an unfiltered mercury arc source.

I used the term 'quantum yield' to indicate the efficiency
of the photodecomposition process. It must be recognized that
the absorption of light does not lead to decomposition in every
case, even though the light may have sufficient energy to break
chemical bonds. The energy absorbed by the molecule leads to
excitation. In addition to decomposition, loss of energy from
the excited state may occur by fluorescence, excitation of
another molecule, etc. Dissociation of a bond represents only
one of the possible modes of energy loss.

How Can Some of the Limitations be Overcome?

The requirement that the radiation contain energy of
sufficiently short wavelengths to cause dissociation of a chemical
bond applies only to the direct absorption of energy by the
reacting molecule; alternative processes can facilitate the induction of photochemical reaction by light of longer wavelengths.

Sensitization represents an example of such a process.
Amitrole is resistant to the direct action of light of wavelengths
greater than 260 nm, it begins to absorb light at shorter wavelengths, and it is photochemically stable. However, in the
presence of riboflavin, amitrole in aqueous solution is rapidly
degraded by light of wavelengths above 300 nm (9). Similarly,
the cyclodiene insecticides in the presence of acetone, which
absorbs light at 290 nm, undergo photochemical reactions.

Sensitized processes involve the transfer of energy from a molecule that has absorbed light and become excited to a higher energy state (usually a "triplet" state). Collisions that take place during this relatively long-lived "triplet" state result in transfer of energy from the excited molecule to a second molecule, which becomes the reactant. Thus, photochemical reaction occurs without direct absorption of light by the reacting molecule.

Another type of energy transfer involves "charge transfer" mechanisms. For example, the photodecomposition of halogenated aromatic compounds such as DDT is facilitated in the presence of amines. Halobenzenes function as electron acceptors in the formation of excited charge-transfer complexes with amines, and photolysis of the charge-transfer complexes may occur at much lower wavelengths than are required for the halogenated compounds alone.

Sensitizers are abundant in "natural" waters and account for the enhanced rates of photolysis of pollutants in streams and rivers. Even though the body of water may appear opaque or dark-colored to the observer, rates of photolysis near the surface are more rapid than in distilled water. The nature of "natural" photosensitizers has received attention. Ross and Crosby (10) examined the photooxidation of aldrin and found that in the presence or absence of light of wavelengths greater than 300 nm, aldrin (10 μg/1.) was stable to light in demineralized water. Aldrin does not absorb light above 250 nm, but in the presence of 0.1% of the triplet sensitizers, acetone or acetaldehyde, aldrin was photooxidized to dieldrin. Singlet oxygen did not appear to be implicated in this conversion, nor were photo-isomerization products detected in these experiments. It was suggested that the formation of a photochemically generated oxidant such as peracetic acid might be responsible for the conversion. The ability of relatively involatile oxidants to bring about such reactions was suggested by experiments in sterilized water obtained from rice paddies. It appeared un-likely in this case that volatile compounds would remain after vacuum evaporation; nevertheless 25% of the aldrin was converted to dieldrin in 36 hours irradiation.

The effect of physical state has also been studied to some extent. The interaction of a molecule with a surface modifies the physical and chemical properties of the molecule through the effects of polar or nonpolar groups at the interface. If the molecule is irradiated, it will display modified photochemical behavior because the energy relations between excited electronic states will have been changed. As examples, the ultraviolet spectra of anilines and phenols in hexane were measured in the presence and absence of silica. The shifts in absorption maxima can be rationalized in terms of hydrogen bonding (11). The changes in absorption spectrum produced when a molecule is adsorbed on a solid will also change its photochemical behavior.

Soil appears to exert a protective effect, but silica may en-
hance photolysis.

Korte and his coworkers (12,13) reported the mineralization
of a number of compounds exposed to ultraviolet irradiation in an
oxygen stream. The source of light was a high pressure lamp
(125 W) housed in a pyrex cold finger. It was found that the
rate of conversion was greater if the compounds were adsorbed on
particulate matter than if they were deposited as solids or thin
films. The experimental arrangement permitted irradiation of the
material adsorbed on silica gel; the silica gel was mixed
continuously by a rotating drum surrounding the lamp housing.
Initially, it was found that certain cyclodiene pesticides and
their photoisomerization products were completely decomposed
(12) on irradiation in the solid state. Hexachlorobenzene,
pentachlorobenzene, pentachlorophenol, 1,1,1-trichloro-2,2-bis(p-
chlorophenyl)ethane (DDT), 1,1-dichloro-2,2-bis(p-chlorophenyl)-
ethylene (DDE), 2,2',4,4',5,5'-hexachlorobiphenyl, and 2,2',4,5'-
tetrachlorobiphenyl were adsorbed on quartz and irradiated
(Table I).

Table I. Irradiation of pentachlorophenol, DDT and DDE on 100 g
silica gel (wavelength > 290 nm) (12).

	Initial Quantity	Amount Recovered			
		4 days		7 days	
Compound	mg	mg	%	mg	%
PCP	102	26	25	12	12
DDT	385	298	77	255	66
DDE *	362	91	25	69	19

* Also detected dichlorobenzophenone, 38 mg;
  trichlorobenzophenone, 7 mg

The rate of disappearance of the compounds was measured, and in
some cases the quantity of CO_2 and HCl evolved was also determined.
It was considered that the rate of disappearance was not
accounted for by the formation of organic photoproducts, nor
could it be attributed to volatilization. These findings may
have an important bearing on the fate of pesticides adsorbed on
particulate matter.

What Products are Formed in Photochemical Reactions of Pesticides?

In practice, we are concerned with the rate of photodecomposition and also with the nature of the products. Photolysis
of halogenated compounds often leads to dehalogenated products,
presumably via a process of hydrogen abstraction from the
solvent by a completely dissociated molecule or excited complex

between solute and solvent. The tables show some results of our own investigations of the photolysis of several chlorinated aromatic compounds (14,15) (Tables II - V).

Table II. Photolysis of chlorophenol methyl ethers in methanol (1g/L, wavelength > 260 nm) (14,15).

Time	Recovery of $ClC_6H_4OCH_3$ (%)			Yield of $C_6H_5OCH_3$ (%)		
	o	m	p	o	m	p
4 h	45	+	7	54	54	70
8 h	13	−	+	83	54	76

Table III. Photolysis of chlorotoluenes in methanol (1g/L, wavelength > 260 nm) (14,15).

Time	Recovery of $ClC_6H_4CH_3$ (%)			Yield of $C_6H_5CH_3$ (%)		
	o	m	p	o	m	p
4 h	5	13	61	67	61	21
8 h	+	+	37	60	66	37

Table IV. Photolysis of chlorobenzonitriles in methanol (1g/L, wavelength > 260 nm) (14,15).

	Amount Recovered (%)		Product * (%)	
	4 h	8 h	4 h	8 h
2,6-Dichloro-benzonitrile	57	36	27	37
2-Chloro-benzonitrile	82	80	13	17

*Formed by loss of 1 Cl atom.

Table V. Photolysis of chlorobenzoic acids in methanol (0.5 g/L, wavelength > 260 nm, 8 h irradiation) (14,15).

	Amount Recovered (%)	Yield of C_6H_5COOH (%)
o	−	100
m	9	52
p	37	60

It is not easy to predict photochemical reactivity in terms of
the known electronic effects of substituent groups. The excited
state in halogen loss is probably a singlet, and little information exists concerning electron distribution in this state.

Several workers have investigated the rates of formation
and the products formed by the nucleophilic displacement of
halogens and other substituents under the influence of light.
One of the earliest studies was concerned with the enhancement of
the rate of replacement of chlorine by the hydroxyl group of
chloracetic acid under ultraviolet light -- investigated by
von Euler in 1916 (16). Crosby (17 , and this Symposium) has
discussed examples of photonucleophilic reactions of pesticides
and has cited the photodecomposition of nitrofen, fenaminosulf
and other pesticides in water among a number of examples. Because light facilitates such displacement reactions, their study
should be extended to determine whether the enhancement of
reaction rates can be put to practical use.

There is now a substantial volume of literature describing
the isolation and identification of irradiation products of
pesticides. Many earlier studies were performed under ill-de-
fined conditions. Subsequent studies were carried out to determine products under "environmental" conditions, in order to
provide information for regulatory agencies. Other laboratory
studies of photochemical reactions of pesticides were conducted
for "academic" reasons. However, we recognize that the processes
are complex. Initial photochemical reactions yield one or more
products that may undergo subsequent photochemical or thermal
reactions, so a complex mixture of products results. There may
be an accumulation of photostable materials. In very dilute
solution in the presence of oxygen it is likely that substantial
degradation of the molecule will occur.

Mechanistic organic photochemistry is an intellectually
stimulating pursuit. Unfortunately it is still in a relatively
primitive state. To quote from a review by H. E. Zimmerman
(18): "Despite the increasing number of known photochemical
reactions the total number of well-established photochemical
transformations is infinitesimal compared with that in ground
state chemistry .... further, our understanding of the factors
which control photochemical reactions is still quite primitive...
more complex calculations are not needed, a new approach is
needed.
  "Finally, totally new methods of determining photochemical
reaction mechanisms are needed; the number is really quite small
when compared with those developed for use in ground state
organic chemistry."

Mechanistic studies of pesticide photochemistry are sparse;
the major effort has usually been to isolate and identify photoproducts. This can readily be understood in terms of immediate
objectives, since concern that the photoproducts may become
environmental pollutants or demonstrate toxicity has been a major

reason for undertaking their identification. Some indication of
the qualitative significance of these photoproducts may have
been obtained, but more precise quantitative information has been
obtained in only a few cases.

Kinetic analysis presents an extremely important and complex problem. However, few photochemical studies of pesticides
have been concerned with the measurement of reaction rates. For
this reason the work of the EPA group in Athens, Georgia, has
been particularly valuable in establishing a quantitative treatment that allows prediction of photolysis rates under solar
irradiation (19). This group has approached the problem of
determining the lifetime of organic pollutants irradiated in
aquatic systems. Dealing with the process of direct photolysis,
they have derived mathematical expressions as a basis for
judgment as to whether a given compound will appear as a
significant residue in the aquatic environment and have computed
"photolysis rates" of a number of compounds. ("Photolysis
rate" here implies the photolytic conversion of the starting
material over unit time.) Solar intensity and the attenuation
of light in natural waters were used to calculate energy inputs.
Quantum yield data and absorption coefficients of the material
in question were used in a computer-based calculation of photolysis rates. The figures shown in Table VI indicate the values
obtained for DDE (19).

Table VI. Photolysis half-life calculated for DDE near the
surface of water body (19).

Season	Half-life
Spring	1.4 days
Summer	0.94
Fall	2.4
Winter	61

These calculations were verified experimentally for dilute solutions. In high concentrations the computed half-lives are
longer as one approaches the situation in which all the incident
light is absorbed. The solvent is responsible for some energy
absorption, so half-life increases with increasing depth. Within
the range of assumptions, there was reasonable correspondence
between experimentally determined rates and those obtained by
computation (+ 30%). Even in the absence of quantum yield data,
minimum half-lives can be calculated from the absorption spectrum.

Many environmental variables limit the value of the computation. However, in a waste-disposal facility, most of these
variables could be controlled. Thus, the data and computations
present a basis for a feasibility study, because necessary
energy input and photolytic half-lives can be calculated from
data obtained in the laboratory. This approach merits attention,

and initial data must be accumulated to make further evaluation possible.

Costs

Practical attempts to evaluate the techniques are few. The cost figures provided are of interest but are usually out of date.

In a report issued by the Atomic Energy Commission, Ballantine et al. ([20]) discussed the practicality of using atomic radiation for wastewater treatment. The applications that they suggested were the improvement of sludge handling, total destruction of organics, disinfection, and the selective removal of refractories or specific compounds. The last application is of particular interest in this symposium. The refractories in waste water are organic compounds not efficiently removed by primary treatment. They could include chlorinated phenol, lignins, and other slowly biodegradable compounds. Their concentration in municipal wastewaters ranges from 10 PPM to occasional high values of 100 PPM. In industrial wastes, higher values are encountered. The calculated cost of radiation treatment for 1000 gallon containing 10 PPM was $0.11; this increased to $1.10 if the concentration of pollutant was 1000 PPM. These costs were based on disappearance of the refractory compound, not on total oxidation, which must be accomplished by further treatment.

The question of using ultraviolet irradiation for the removal of refractory compounds from water was addressed by Bulla and Edgerley ([21]). They found that aldrin, dieldrin and endrin in dilute aqueous solutions were degraded by light of 253.7 nm wavelength. Time, depth and intensity of radiation were related to the degradation of individual compounds, and cost estimates were made for 50 percent degradation of pesticides at 10 cm depth. These were $24 for aldrin solutions, $74 for dieldrin and $57 for endrin per million gallons, for concentrations of 20 to 25 µg per liter. These figures could possibly be reduced if the reactor design were improved, and many compounds less resistant to photolysis could be processed at lower cost. Irradiation in the presence of oxidants such as chlorine or oxygen may be more effective; however, the formation of chlorinated organic molecules as end products is undesirable.

There is need for further study of the comparative costs of waste disposal by incineration, biological treatment, soil disposal, ocean disposal and irradiation. In addition to dollar costs, other factors, particularly environmental impacts, must also be taken into account. Ultimately, it is to be hoped that technological developments will permit the efficient utilization of solar energy to degrade chemical wastes; such a process might involve the use of photolysis alone or as a preparatory step to achieve partial breakdown of refractory molecules before wastes are subjected to microbiological degradation.

Literature Cited

1. Lawless, E. W., Ferguson, T. L., and Meiners, A. F. "Guidelines for the Disposal of Small Quantities of Unused Pesticides'." EPA-67012-75-057, National Environmental Research Center, U. S. Environmental Protection Agency, Cincinnati, Ohio. 1975.
2. Kennedy, M. V., Stojanovic, B. J., and Shuman, F. L., Jr., Residue Rev. (1967) 29, 89–104.
3. Plimmer, J. R., and Kearney, P. C. 165th Natl. Mtg. Amer. Chem. Soc., Dallas (April 1973).
4. Kennedy, M. V., Stojanovic, B. J., and Shuman, F. L., Jr., J. Environ. Qual (1972) 1, 63–65.
5. Peakall, D. B., and Lincer, J. L., BioScience (1970) 20, 958–964.
6. Plimmer, J. R., Klingebiel, U. I., Crosby, D. G., and Wong, A. S. Advances in Chemistry No. 120. pp. 44–54. American Chemical Society, Washington, D.C. 1973.
7. Crosby, D. G., and Wong, A. S., Science (1977) 195, 1337–1338.
8. Turro, N. J., J. Chem. Ed. (1967) 44, 536–537.
9. Plimmer, J. R., Kearney, P. C., Kaufman, D. D., and Guardia, F. S., J. Agr. Food Chem. (1967) 15, 996–997.
10. Roos, R. D., and Crosby, D. C., Chemosphere (1975) 5, 277–282.
11. Plimmer, J. R., in "Fate of Pesticides in Environment", Vol. 6 of "Pesticide Chemistry", A. S. Tahori, ed. pp. 47–76. Gordon and Breach Science Publishers, New York and London. 1972.
12. Gäb, S., Parlar, H., Nitz, S., Hastert, K., and Korte, F., Chemosphere (1974) 3, 183–186.
13. Gäb, S., Nitz, H., Parlar, H., and Korte, F., Chemosphere (1975) 4, 251–256.
14. Plimmer, J. R., Residue Rev. (1971) 33, 47–74.
15. Plimmer, J. R., and Hummer, B. E., 155th Am. Chem.Soc. Nat. Meeting, San Francisco (1968).
16. von Euler, H., Chem. Ber. (1916) 49, 1366–1371.
17. Crosby, D. G., Moilanen, K. W., Nakagawa, M., and Wong, A. S., U.S.-Japan Seminar on the Environmental Toxicology of Pesticides, Ioso, Japan, Oct. 1971.
18. Zimmerman, H. E., Science (1976) 191, 523–528.
19. Zepp, R. A., and Clive, D. M., Environ. Sci. Technol. (1977) 11, 359–366.
20. Ballantine, D. S., Miller, L. A., Bishop, D. F., and Rohrman, F. A. Atomic Energy Commission Report. 1970.
21. Bulla, C. D., III, and Edgerley, E., Jr., J. Water Pollut. Contr. Fed. (1968) 40, 546–556.

MARCH 9, 1978

3

Catalytic Hydrodechlorination of Polychlorinated Hydrocarbons

WILMER L. KRANICH, RENE B. LaPIERRE[1], LASZLO GUCZI[2], and
ALVIN H. WEISS

Department of Chemical Engineering, Worcester Polytechnic Institute,
Worcester, MA 01609

Catalytic hydrodechlorination is one of the methods
under consideration for conversion of chlorinated pesticides and other environmentally undesirable chlorinated
compounds into environmentally acceptable products.

LaPierre, Guczi, Wu, Kranich and Weiss ($\underline{1}$-$\underline{3}$) have
reported on the reactions of DDT (and its derivative by
simple dehydrochlorination, DDE), and Aroclor 1248 (a
typical polychlorinated biphenyl). Both liquid and gas
phase reactions were studied over a range of pressures
from 1 to 50 bar, temperatures from 20 to 230°C and with
both nickel and palladium catalysts. Solvents for liquid
phase reactions included ethanol and xylene, and both cal-
cium and sodium hydroxides were used as hydrochloric acid
(by-product) acceptors. In this paper additional hydrodechlorination data are given for Dieldrin, Aldrin, and
Toxaphene (chlorinated camphene).

Chemistry of Hydrodechlorination

PCB. The catalyzed hydrodechlorination reactions to
remove chlorine from PCBs proceed one step at a time in a
consecutive manner. $\emptyset\emptyset_n$ represents a biphenyl nucleus
substituted with n chlorine atoms

$$\emptyset\emptyset_5 \xrightarrow[-\text{HCl}]{\overset{k_{54}}{+\text{H}_2}} \emptyset\emptyset_4 \xrightarrow[-\text{HCl}]{\overset{k_{43}}{+\text{H}_2}} \emptyset\emptyset_3 \xrightarrow[-\text{HCl}]{\overset{k_{32}}{+\text{H}_2}} \emptyset\emptyset_2 \xrightarrow[-\text{HCl}]{\overset{k_{21}}{+\text{H}_2}} \emptyset\emptyset_1 \xrightarrow[-\text{HCl}]{\overset{k_{10}}{+\text{H}_2}} \emptyset\emptyset_0$$

Kinetics are well represented by a series of successive
reactions. If simple first order rate constants (k_{mn}) are
calculated relative to the first step, a single set of
constants represents the data over the range of 60-130°C
at 50 bar hydrogen pressure for liquid-phase reactions

[1] Current address: Mobil Research Corporation, Princeton, NJ
[2] Current address: Institute of Isotopes, Hungarian Academy of Sciences, Budapest, Hungary

in ethanol solvent with nickel catalyst (Girdler G49) and NaOH as acid acceptor. Product distributions based on $k_{54}=1$, $k_{43}=0.40$, $k_{32}=0.23$, $k_{21}=0.36$, and $k_{10}=0.40$ are shown in Figure 1 superimposed on the experimental data.

DDT-DDE. In the presence of sodium hydroxide in ethanol solvent, DDT is quickly converted non-catalytically to DDE.

$$\underset{\text{(DDT)}}{\text{Cl}\emptyset - \overset{\text{H}}{\underset{\text{CCl}_3}{\text{C}}} - \emptyset\text{Cl}} \quad\xrightarrow{\text{-HCl}}\quad \underset{\text{(DDE)}}{\text{Cl}\emptyset - \overset{\text{||}}{\underset{\text{CCl}_2}{\text{C}}} - \emptyset\text{Cl}}$$

The subsequent reactions of DDE are more complex. They not only involve consecutive aromatic hydrodechlorination but also parallel reactions in which olefinic chlorines are removed and the associated olefin is saturated without intermediate desorption from the catalyst. Note in the following reaction network that as many as five hydrogen molecules react in one step. The numbers shown are first order rate constants relative to the total rate of reaction of DDE by all four paths, for liquid phase reaction with hydrogen at 50 bar, Ni catalyst, over the temperature range 20-100°C. These constants have been used to calculate the product distribution shown in Figure 2, superimposed on the experimental data.

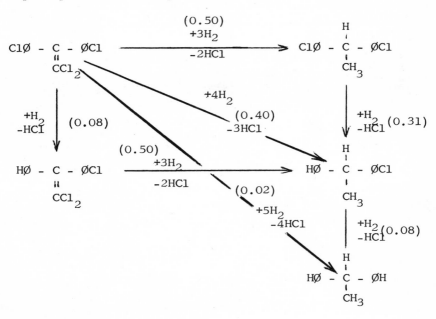

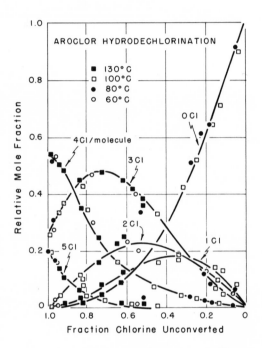

Figure 1. Product distribution vs. chlorine conversion for hydrodechlorination of PCB (Aroclor 1248)

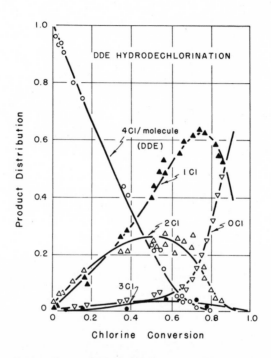

Figure 2. Product distribution vs. chlorine conversion for hydrodechlorination of DDE (DDT)

Aldrin-Dieldrin. The structures of Aldrin and its corresponding epoxide Dieldrin are:

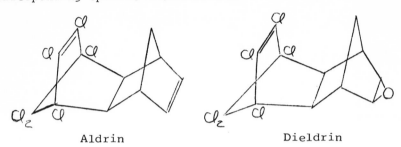

Aldrin   Dieldrin

Experimental data on relative mole fraction of hydro-dechlorination products of Aldrin and Dieldrin are shown in Figures 3 and 4. These data are for liquid phase re-action in ethanol at 50 bar hydrogen and 130°C with NaOH as acid acceptor. The catalyst is again nickel (Girdler G49). Experimental procedures are similar to those des-cribed for DDE (2) and Aroclor 1248 (3). The data do not lend themselves to simple kinetic analysis.

For Aldrin, hydrodechlorination appears to proceed as follows:

$$C_{12}H_8Cl_6 \xrightarrow[-HCl]{+2H_2} C_{12}H_{11}Cl_5 \xrightarrow[-HCl]{+H_2} C_{12}H_{12}Cl_4$$

$$\xrightarrow[-2HCl]{+3H_2} \qquad \xrightarrow[-2HCl]{+3H_2}$$

$$C_{12}H_{15}Cl_3 \qquad\qquad C_{12}H_{16}Cl_2$$

First an olefinic group in Aldrin hydrogenates (the epoxide in Dieldrin is not affected at these conditions) in a step simultaneous with removal of a highly active geminal di-chloride. The molecule then loses in one step its olefinic chlorine atoms and hydrogenates that olefinic bond.

For Dieldrin the principal reaction path seems to be similar but simpler, since there is no olefinic bond to hydrogenate.

$$C_{12}H_8Cl_6O \xrightarrow[-HCl]{+H_2} C_{12}H_9Cl_5O \xrightarrow[-HCl]{+H_2} C_{12}H_{10}Cl_4O$$

The last highly unreactive chlorines to be removed are the aliphatic chlorines, and the consequence of their very low reactivity is that Aldrin and Dieldrin are not readily completely stripped to the corresponding hydro-carbon skeletons.

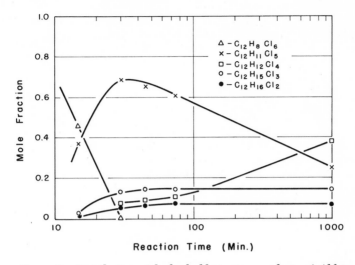

Figure 3. Distribution of hydrodechlorination products of Aldrin vs. reaction time

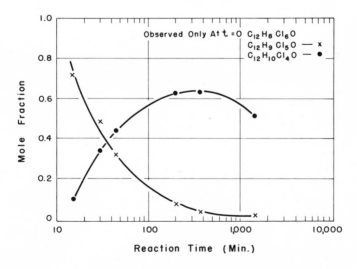

Figure 4. Distribution of hydrodechlorination products of Dieldrin vs. reaction time

Toxaphene. Toxaphene is a mixture of highly chlorinated derivatives of camphene. A typical compound which has
been isolated from a representative toxaphene mixture is a
heptachlorobornane.

In hydrodechlorination the geminal chlorines are
readily attacked but the remaining aliphatic chlorines are
quite stable. As with Dieldrin and Aldrin, complete removal of chlorine from the hydrocarbon skeleton is very
difficult. Experimental results for toxaphene hydrodechlorination are given in Table I.

TABLE I
TOXAPHENE HYDRODECHLORINATION AT 100°C, 50 BAR
(4-6 wt % Toxaphene in Ethanol; 10gm Toxaphene/gm catalyst,
Ni on Kieselguhr)

Reaction Time (hr)	2	4	19
Chlorine atoms/molecule	Distribution (%)		
0	16.5	32.4	37.2
1	21.4	29.0	25.8
2	29.9	20.3	24.2
3	9.4	2.8	1.2
4	8.5	11.6	10.5
5	5.5	2.0	1.1
6	6.1	1.9	
7	1.5		
8	1.2		

Based on its 68% (wt) chlorine, the original Toxaphene
contained an average of 7.8 chlorine atoms per molecule

Hydrodechlorination Process. A process is proposed
based on the laboratory studies, which is capable of dechlorinating DDT and PCBs to any desired level and partially dechlorinating Dieldrin, Aldrin and Toxaphene.
     A conceptualized flow sheet is given in Figure 5.
The materials to be treated are charged as a batch to a
rotary (tumbling) extractor. The organic materials to be
hydrodechlorinated are extracted with hot ethanol and
pumped to the reactor. During the extraction phase the
reactor contents are boiled at atmospheric pressure and
the ethanol is evaporated, condensed and returned to the
extractor until the containers and inert materials remaining in the extractor are free of pesticides. Ethanol may
be recovered from the cleaned solid waste either by a
final extraction with water or by heating sufficiently to

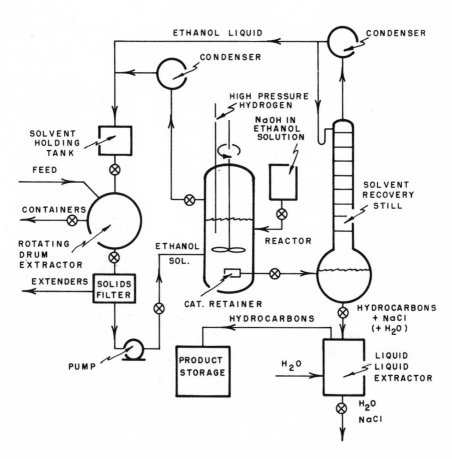

Figure 5. Hydrodechlorination process flow diagram

flash it off.

Sodium hydroxide (dissolved in ethanol) is then added to the reactor and the system is pressurized with hydrogen. Hydrodechlorination proceeds in the presence of the nickel catalyst, which is retained in the reactor from batch to batch. NaOH solution is added automatically in response to decreasing alkalinity of the reacting solution.

When the reaction reaches the desired degree of completion as indicated by the demand for NaOH solution, the liquid contents are strained through the catalyst retention screen to the solvent recovery still. Here some or all of the ethanol is boiled off, purified in a column as necessary to remove water or other impurities and returned to the solvent holding tank.

The products containing NaCl and a slight excess of NaOH are extracted with water to remove the soluble inorganics. Use or disposal of the organic products depends on the degree of dechlorination, complexity of the feed and product, and the usefulness of the product for other purposes (e.g. as a plasticizer or chemical raw material).

Reactor Design. Laboratory results permit estimation of the reaction time required to reach a given degree of chlorine removal and the distribution of products. For reactions at 100°C, 50 bar pressure, 61% Ni on kieselguhr catalyst, 1-6% (weight) reactant in ethanol, 10-40 grams reactant per gram catalyst, the percentage of original chlorine remaining as a function of time is given approximately by Figure 6 for DDE, PCB (Aroclor 1248) and Toxaphene. Dieldrin-Aldrin data are not included, since their hydrodechlorinations were run at 130°C.

All of the curves show rapid initial replacement of some of the chlorine by hydrogen followed by slower reaction. Since several types of chlorine bonding exist, the more labile types (aromatic, olefinic, geminal) are attacked before the very stable aliphatic chlorines.

With Dieldrin and Aldrin, initial reaction of geminal chlorines is rapid, but aliphatic monochloro bonds are only very slowly substituted by hydrogen. If further chlorine removal from these compounds is required (rather than simply the reduction in toxicity accompanying the rapid initial reaction), more severe operating conditions would be needed.

Figure 2 follows in detail the intermediate reaction products containing the indicated number of chlorine atoms per molecule as a function of the fraction total chlorine removed from DDE. Figure 1 gives the same information for Aroclor 1248, a typical polychlorinated biphenyl. Both of these sets of curves are nearly independent of temperature. Figures 1, 2, and 6 can be treated as design curves to meet a variety of processing objectives for these two

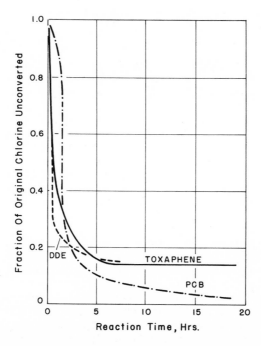

Figure 6. Chlorine conversion vs. time (liquid-phase hydrodechlorination at 100°C, 50 bar, 1–6% (wt) in ethanol, 10–40 g reactant/g 61% Ni on kieselguhr catalyst)

materials such as removal of a given fraction of original
chlorine, conversion of a given fraction of starting material, or maximizing the yield of a particular intermediate.

Acknowledgement

Financial support for this study was provided by the
United States Environmental Protection Agency under EPA
contract R 802-857-01 "Catalytic Conversion of Hazardous
and Toxic Chemicals". Dr. E. Biron helped in the work.

Abstract

A conceptual process is described for the catalytic
hydrodechlorination of chlorinated pesticides (e.g. DDT,
Aldrin, Dieldrin, and Toxaphene), and other environmentally
undesirable compounds (e.g. polychlorinated biphenyls, PCB).
Experimental studies show that chlorines can in general be
catalytically replaced by hydrogen to any desired extent.
Products are generally high boiling oils which may be useful or readily burned.
Reaction models are proposed and relative rate constants determined for several hydrodechlorinations.   In
general, olefinic and aromatic chlorines are more easily
removed than aliphatic chlorines. Highly bridged, non-
planar molecules like Dieldrin and Aldrin are very difficult to hydrodechlorinate completely.

Literature Cited

1) LaPierre, R.B., Wu, D., Kranich, W.L., and Weiss, A.H.
    J. Catal., (1978), (In Press)
2) LaPierre, R.B., Guczi, L., Kranich, W.L., and Weiss,
    A.H., J. Catal. (1978), (Paper on DDE - In Press)
3) LaPierre, R.B., Guczi, L., Kranich, W.L., and Weiss,
    A.H., J. Catal. (1978), (Paper on PCB - In Press)
See Also: LaPierre, R.B., Biron, E., Wu, D., Guczi, L.,
    Kranich, W.L., and Weiss, A.H., "Catalytic Conversion
    of Hazardous and Toxic Chemicals: Pesticides and
    Related Substances," Document No. PB 262 804, EPA-
    600/3-77-018, January 1977. National Technical In-
    formation Service, U.S. Department of Commerce, 5285
    Port Royal Road, Springfield, Va. See also "Catalytic
    Hydrodechlorination of Polychlorinated Pesticides and
    Related Substances: An Executive Summary," EPA-600/
    8-77-013, September 1977.

MARCH 23, 1978

Photodegradation of Halogenated Xanthene Dyes

JAMES R. HEITZ

Department of Biochemistry, Mississippi Agricultural and Forestry Experiment
Station, Mississippi State University, Mississippi State, MS 39762

W. W. WILSON
Department of Chemistry, Mississippi State University, Mississippi State, MS 39762

At the outset, the work of several other of our colleagues
who aided in the collection of the data used in this presenta-
tion should be acknowledged. They are Dr. Gajanan Pimprikar,
Mr. Richard D. Vincent, Mr. John E. Fondren, Jr., Mr. William A.
Peoples, II, and Mr. Kashinath Nag--all of Mississippi State
University.

Since this symposium is devoted to "Disposal and Decontamination of Pesticides," it is appropriate to justify the inclu-
sion of xanthene dyes as pesticides before discussing our work
on the degradation and detoxification of these molecules.

Within the last six years, it has been reported that when
insects were fed certain dyes and subsequently exposed to visible
light, a toxic reaction was observed (1-10). An example of this
toxicity in insects caused by the synergistic effects of visible light and dyes is shown in Table I. Imported fire ants were
field collected and maintained in the mound soil in the laboratory on a water diet for seven days. After that time, approximately 100 specimens were put into glass petri dishes. A piece
of wet filter paper provided moisture. Aqueous sucrose solutions, to which variable amounts of rose bengal had been added,
were placed in plastic cups containing a small piece of cotton
dental wicking. This served as the food source as well as the
means of administering the dye to the insects. After incubating
the fire ants in the petri dishes for 24 hours, they were exposed
to 3800 $\mu W/cm^2$ visible light from two 40W General Electric cool
white fluorescent lamps. This is approximately 10 percent of
the light available on a sunny day. The data are presented as
percent mortality ± one standard deviation at 1, 2, 3, 4, and 6
hrs of light exposure at four rose bengal concentrations ranging
from 4.9 x 10^{-3}M down to 4.9 x 10^{-4}M. There is an inverse
relationship between the feeding concentration and the LT_{50}
value as well as the time of light exposure and the LD_{50} value.
Later studies have shown that it is a superior technique to
present the insect mortality data as a function not only of the

Table I

Mortality of the Imported Fire Ant
as a Function of Dye Concentration and Time

Rose Bengal (10^{-3} M)	Exposure Time (hr)[a]					LT_{50}[b]	r
	1	2	3	4	6		
4.90	42.1 (±7.6)	64.7 (±9.2)	88.7 (±8.9)	94.8 (±3.7)	99.7 (±0.7)	0.7	.90
2.46	30.5 (±16.4)	45.1 (±21.8)	59.8 (±29.3)	73.6 (±17.7)	89.0 (±14.8)	2.4	.99
0.98	7.4 (±4.9)	14.5 (±7.1)	23.6 (±4.3)	34.3 (±7.0)	60.7 (±7.4)	5.2	.98
0.49	3.7 (±2.6)	6.1 (±3.6)	13.6 (±7.9)	23.8 (±14.4)	44.4 (±20.6)	7.0	.97
LD_{50}[c] (10^{-3} M)	5.5	3.5	2.5	1.8	0.24		
r	.96	.97	.98	.96	.9		

[a]Data presented as percent mean mortality ± one standard deviation.
[b]Determined by linear regression of mortality data at a known dose level.
[c]Determined by linear regression of mortality data during a known time interval.
(Reproduced from Reference 3.)

dietary dye concentration; but also as a function of the tissue dye level.

The first toxic reaction involved the synergistic effect of visible light and dyes on the insect. A second dye induced toxic reaction in insects was discovered in our laboratory which occurred in the absence of light and was considerably slower than the previously discussed light-catalyzed reaction. Figure 1 shows the probit mortality for three insect species exposed to a 5 x 10^{-3}M rose bengal food source in the absence of light. Probits are merely a linear transformation of the sigmoidal death curve. The feeding medium for the boll weevil (X) was an artificial diet essentially developed by Lindig and Malone (11). A one percent sucrose solution was used for the imported fire ant (O). A two percent milk-sucrose solution was used for the house fly (●). Preliminary studies of the face fly indicate that the susceptibility of this insect closely parallels that of the house fly. There appears to be a wide divergence in the susceptibility of different species of insect to the light-independent toxic mechanism.

The mechanism which appears to be operative in the light-catalyzed reaction is shown in Figure 2. The dye in the ground singlet state absorbs a photon of visible light (a) and is excited to some higher singlet state. If the dye was raised to the second excited singlet state or some higher state, it would give off the excess energy as heat (h) and decay to the first excited singlet state. The lifetime of the first excited singlet state is on the order of nanoseconds. There are three main fates of the dye molecule in this state: 1) it may give off the excess energy as heat (h) and return to the ground singlet state; 2) it may give off the excess energy as light (f) and return to the ground singlet state--this is defined as fluorescence; 3) it may go from a singlet state to a triplet state by inverting the spin of an electron--this is called intersystem crossing. If the dye moves to the triplet state by intersystem crossing, it has reached a more stable state with a lifetime greater than microseconds. If one ignores the reverse intersystem crossing back to the first excited singlet state, there are three main fates of the dye molecule in this state: 1) it may give off the excess energy as heat (h) and return to the ground singlet state; 2) it may give off the energy as light (p) and return to the ground singlet state--this is defined as phosphorescence; 3) it may give the energy to a second molecule, in this case, oxygen. The dye thereby returns to the ground singlet state and the oxygen is raised to the first excited state. This use of the dye molecule to absorb light energy and transfer it to oxygen to form the very reactive and toxic singlet oxygen is integral to dye-sensitized photooxidation and probably to the dye-induced toxicity of visible light in insects. Since movement of the singlet dye to the triplet dye is critical to the toxic reaction, the more phosphorescent the dye is, the

more toxic it should be. Within the xanthene series of dyes,
this has been observed. Decreasing toxicity generally corresponds
with decreasing halogen content. Figure 3 shows the structure
of the xanthene dyes most studied to date. Rose bengal, the
best sensitizer to date in all cases, contains iodine at A and
chlorine at B. Phloxin B, currently being tested on the
imported fire ant, contains bromine at A and chlorine at B.
Erythrosin B, currently under test with two Musca species,
contains iodine at A and hydrogen at B. Eosin yellowish
contains bromine at A and hydrogen at B. The two dyes shown
ineffective in every study to date are fluorescein, containing
hydrogen at both A and B and rhodamine B, containing hydrogen
at A and B and with two wing oxygens replaced by diethylamino
groups. This inspection of the dye structures also may serve
to explain the observed similarity between the light-dependent
and light-independent mechanisms. Increased halogen content
may increase the toxicity of the light-dependent mechanism by
increasing the triplet state populations. Increased halogen
content may increase the toxicity of the light-independent
mechanism similar to an organochlorine mechanism. There would
be two entirely different mechanisms, but inextricably linked
together through the halogen content of the dye molecules
themselves.

Having shown the pesticidal potential of the xanthene
dyes, it now becomes important to investigate the degradation
of the dyes once they are introduced into the environment.
When nitrogen gas was bubbled through a rose bengal solution
to decrease as far as possible the oxygen concentration in the
solution, then sealed and placed in sunlight for two months, a
straw-colored solution was generated. If the rose bengal
solution was not deoxygenated and was instead left open to the
environment and full sunlight for two months, a clear solution
was generated. The increased availability of oxygen in the
latter case probably facilitated the decolorization reaction.
The extent of the decolorization is shown in Figure 4. The
visible absorption spectrum of rose bengal between 400nm and
600nm is depicted by curve B. Upon photodegradation, the
absorption disappears completely (curve A). At this point the
question remained as to the complexity of the photodegradation
reaction. After a partially complete photodegradation reaction
high performance liquid chromatography was used to investigate
the composition of the solution. Figure 5 shows pure rose
bengal on the left and the partially degraded rose bengal on
the right. These traces, and the ones that follow, were
generated using a Waters M6000A pump, a U6K injector, a µBondapak
reverse phase C_{18} column, and a 440 UV-visible detector. The
detector was set at 546nm. The samples were eluted with a 70
percent methanol-30 percent 0.01M ammonium acetate buffer. It
is obvious that as the rose bengal photodegrades, a multiplicity
of products appears. Further, due to the decrease in relative

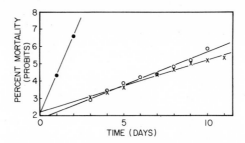

Figure 1.   Light-independent mortality as a function of time of exposure to rose bengal in the food supply of the boll weevil (x), the imported fire ant (o), and the house fly (•)

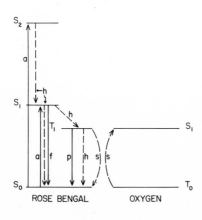

Figure 2.   Scheme suggested for the dye-sensitized photooxidation operative with the substituted xanthene series of dyes. (See text for explanation of symbols. Reproduced from Reference 10).

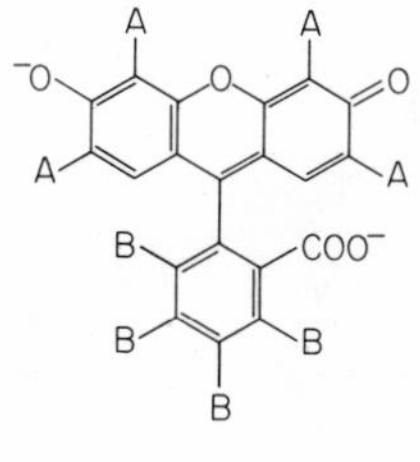

Figure 3.   The molecular structure of the xanthene dyes studied in this work. (See text for explanation of the substituents A and B. Reproduced from Reference 5.)

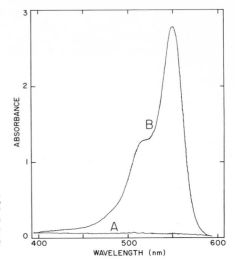

Figure 4. The visible absorbance spectrum of a rose bengal solution which had been photodegraded by sunlight is shown by Trace A. Trace B is the spectrum of the rose bengal solution before exposure to sunlight.

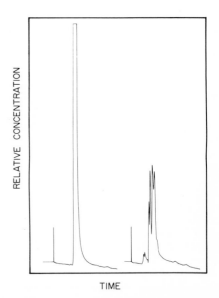

Figure 5. High-performance liquid chromatographic trace of purified rose bengal (left) and partially photodegraded rose bengal (right) observed with a 546-nm absorbance

retention (k') of the products, one can postulate that these products are more polar than rose bengal. Finally, the fact that these products are able to be detected at 546nm and the fact that completely photodegraded rose bengal has no visible absorption, indicates that each of these products is an intermediate in the overall reaction.

Although rose bengal and the photodegraded products do not absorb in the ultraviolet as strongly as in the visible, the UV traces of the liquid chromatographic separation are shown in Figure 6. Pure rose bengal is shown on the left and partially photodegraded rose bengal on the right. Again, it may be seen that all of the products formed during this reaction are more polar; that is, a lower k', than rose bengal itself.

In Figure 7, the two partially degraded rose bengal traces are presented together with the 280nm absorption trace above the 546nm absorption trace. The position of rose bengal on these traces would correspond with the strong doublet on the 546nm trace. The purification and identification of these intermediate compounds is currently an area of prime consideration in our laboratory.

The rate of photodegradation of the xanthene dyes has also been studied. Figure 8 shows the decrease in absorbance at 546nm of solutions of rose bengal as a function of illumination time at 5 light intensities between $1mE/m^2 \cdot sec$ and $6mE/m^2 \cdot sec$. The logarithm of the absorbance is linearly dependent on the time of illumination and is indicative of a first order rate of reaction. The pseudo first order rate constant (k_1) can be calculated for each reaction by the method of half-lives. If the k_1 values are plotted as a function of the light intensity used to generate those values, as shown in Figure 9, one obtains a linear relationship. The slope of that line is k_2, a pseudo second order rate constant, which provides the basis for comparison of the susceptibility to photodegradation of the various dyes (Table II). By this criterion, erythrosin B is the most readily photodegradable with eosin yellowish and rose bengal close behind. The two dyes tested which contain no halogen, rhodamine B and fluorescein, are most resistant to photodegradation. It appears that halogen on the upper ring system facilitates the reaction while halogen presence on the lower ring retards the photodegradation reaction. It may also be mentioned that phosphorescent dyes generally photodegrade while fluorescent dyes do not.

At low dye concentrations, the reaction is clearly first order (Figure 10). As the initial concentration increases, the top line for instance, the initial portion of the reaction is slower than the first order reaction observed at lower concentrations. When the overall reaction is observed at very high concentrations, addition of the two reactions yielded apparent zero order data.

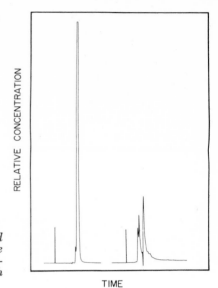

TIME

Figure 6. High-performance liquid chromatographic trace of purified rose bengal (left) and partially photodegraded rose bengal (right) observed with a 280-nm absorbance detector

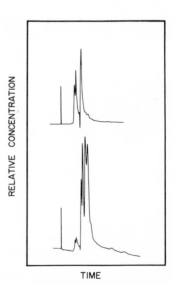

TIME

Figure 7. Direct comparison of partially photodegraded rose-bengal according to 280-nm absorbance (top) and 546-nm absorbance (bottom)

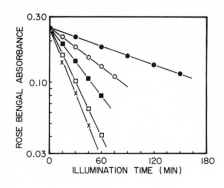

Figure 8. Semi-log plot showing the decrease in absorbance of a rose bengal solution as a function of illumination time. Each trace represents data taken at a different intensity: (●), 1.0; (○), 2.0; (■), 3.5; (□), 5.0; (x), 6.0; $mE/m^2 \cdot sec$.

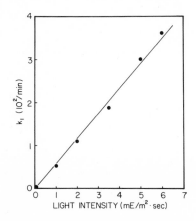

Figure 9. The rate constant k_1 plotted as a function of the incident light intensity

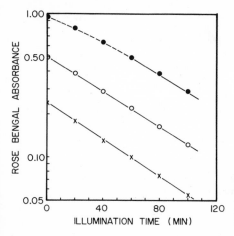

Figure 10. Semi-log plot showing the decrease in absorbance of rose bengal solutions as a function of illumination time. Each trace represents data taken at a different rose bengal concentration: (x), $3.3 \times 10^{-6}M$; (○), $6.6 \times 10^{-6}M$; (●), $13.2 \times 10^{-6}M$.

Figure 11 shows this effect from a different viewpoint. If k_1, calculated from the half-life, is plotted against the initial rose bengal concentration, the reaction rate is found to decrease as the rose bengal concentration increases to about $6 \times 10^{-5}M$, at which point the rate becomes independent of dye concentration. Below $4 \times 10^{-6}M$, as shown in the inset, the rate is also independent of rose bengal concentration. It may be hypothesized that either substrate quenching of the excited state by the dye may cause the decrease in reaction rate or else light is rate limiting at concentrations higher than $6 \times 10^{-5}M$.

Table II

Relative Rates of Hydrolysis

Erythrosin B	12
Eosin Yellowish	10
Rose Bengal	10
Phloxin B	5
Fluorescein	1
Rhodamine B	0

Another question of critical importance to this study is whether the dyes are detoxified during the photodegradation process. Table III shows that completely photodegraded rose bengal was completely ineffective in eliciting the light-catalyzed toxic reaction which was induced by the presence of undegraded rose bengal. Both rose bengal solutions were made up at $7 \times 10^{-6}M$; one was photodegraded in sunlight and the other left in the dark. Both solutions were concentrated to an effective level of $5 \times 10^{-4}M$ before feeding to the house flies for 24 hrs in the dark. After 21 hrs exposure to the fluorescent light, 95 percent mortality was observed due to undegraded rose bengal compared with zero mortality in both photodegraded rose bengal and control populations. A second experiment where the rose bengal concentrations were $2.5 \times 10^{-3}M$, showed similar results. Flies treated with undegraded rose bengal were all dead within 5 hrs of light exposure. There were no dead flies in either the degraded rose bengal or control populations. These results were not all that surprising since the photodegraded rose bengal does not absorb visible light. Table IV, however, shows a key experiment. The photodegraded dye was also incapable of eliciting the light-independent toxic reaction caused by undegraded rose bengal. Upon feeding on $2.5 \times 10^{-3}M$ undegraded rose bengal in the dark, mortality was observed after 72 hrs and by 96 hrs, 90 percent of the flies were dead. There was no toxicity in the other two populations.

Table III

Toxicity to House Flies of Photodegraded and
Undegraded Rose Bengal in the Light

Treatment	Time of Illumination (hr)						
	0	3	12	15	17	19	21
Control	0[a]	0	0	0	0	0	0
Rose Bengal[b]							
Photodegraded	0	0	0	0	0	0	0
Undegraded	0	0	40	55	75	75	95

[a]Data presented as percent mortality where the control was one
chamber of 10 flies and the dye-treated were two chambers of
10 flies each.
[b]Initial rose bengal solutions were 7×10^{-6}M in distilled
water. Photodegraded samples were exposed to sunlight for 3
days, undegraded samples were kept in the dark for same time
period. Dye samples were concentrated to 5×10^{-4}M for administration to flies.

Table IV

Toxicity to House Flies of Photodegraded and
Undegraded Rose Bengal in the Dark

Treatment	Time of Illumination (hr)					
	0	36	60	72	84	96
Control	0[a]	0	0	0	0	0
Rose Bengal[b]						
Photodegraded	0	0	0	0	0	0
Undegraded	0	0	0	0	30	90

[a]Data presented as percent mortality where each treatment was one
chamber of 10 flies each.
[b]Initial rose bengal solutions were 7×10^{-6}M in distilled water.
Photodegraded samples were exposed to sunlight for 3 days,
undegraded samples were kept in the dark for same time period.
Dye samples were concentrated to 2.5×10^{-3}M for administration
to flies.

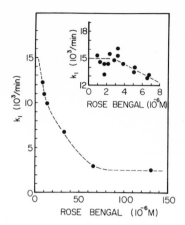

Figure 11. The apparent first-order rate constant k_1 plotted as a function of rose bengal concentration

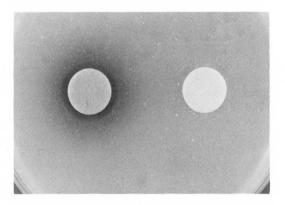

Figure 12. The toxic effect of rose bengal on Stapholococcus aureus (right) as compared with photodegraded rose bengal (left)

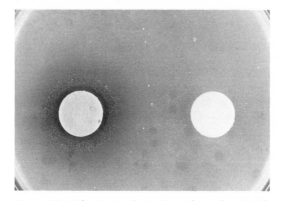

Figure 13. The toxic effect of rose bengal on Bacillus cereus (right) as compared with photodegraded rose bengal (left)

The same question of photodegradation and detoxification
has been studied with respect to bacteria. Figure 12 shows an
agar plate to which Stapholococcus aureus had been added during
preparation. A small disc of filter paper is placed on the agar
plate and the solution to be tested is added to the filter paper.
In this case, 7.75 x 10^{-4} undegraded rose bengal and the same
concentration of photodegraded rose bengal are tested. While
the bacteria grows, the solution will diffuse from the filter
paper out into the agar. If the solution is toxic to the
bacteria, a clear halo of nongrowth will surround the disc.
This is the case with undegraded rose bengal on the left. If
the solution is nontoxic to the bacteria, the growth will
occur right up to the disc. This is the case with the photodegraded rose bengal on the right. It may also be observed that
the growth of the bacteria, Bacillus cereus, is affected by
undegraded rose bengal on the left, but not by photodegraded
rose bengal on the right (Figure 13).

The results of these ongoing investigations have shown that
substituted xanthene dyes may be photodegraded quite effectively
by ordinary visible light similar to the levels found in the
environment. Furthermore, the photodegradation reaction leads
to a complex mixture of intermediates and products. It has also
been shown that the photodegradation products are nontoxic to
both insects and bacteria in both the light-dependent and the
light-independent mechanisms. MAFES Publication No. 8532.

Literature Cited

1.   Yoho, T. P., Butler, L., and Weaver, J. E.   J. Econ. Entomol.
      (1971). 64:972-3.
2.   Yoho, T. P., Weaver, J. E., and Butler, L.   Environ. Entomol.
      (1973). 2:1092-6.
3.   Broome, J. R., Callaham, M. F., Lewis, L. A., Ladner, C. M.,
      and Heitz, J. R. Comp. Biochem. Physiol. (1975). 51C:
      117-21.
4.   Callaham, M. F., Lewis, L. A., Holloman, M. E., Broome,
      J. R., and Heitz, J. R. Comp. Biochem. Physiol.
      (1975). 51C: 123-8.
5.   Callaham, M. F., Broome, J. R., Lindig, O. H., and
      Heitz, J. R. Environ. Entomol. (1975). 4:837-41.
6.   Broome, J. R., Callaham, M. F., and Heitz, J. R.
      Environ. Entomol. (1975). 4:883-6.
7.   Yoho, T. P., Butler, L., and Weaver, J. E.   Environ.
      Entomol. (1976). 5:203-4.
8.   Broome, J. R., Callaham, M. F., Poe, W. E., and Heitz,
      J. R. Chem.-Biol. Interact. (1976). 14:203-6.
9.   Callaham, M. F., Broome, J. R., Poe, W. E., and Heitz,
      J. R. Environ. Entomol. (1977). 6:669-73.
10.   Callaham, M. F., Palmertree, C. O., Broome, J. R., and
      Heitz, J. R. Pest. Biochem. Physiol. (1977). 7:21-7.
11.   Lindig, O. H. and Malone, O. C. J. Econ. Entomol. (1973).
      66:566-7.

Detoxification of Pesticides and Hazardous Wastes by the Microwave Plasma Process

LIONEL J. BAILIN and BARRY L. HERTZLER

Department of Chemistry, Lockheed Palo Alto Research Laboratory, 3251 Hanover Street, Palo Alto, CA 94304

DONALD A. OBERACKER

Solid and Hazardous Waste Research Division, Municipal Environmental Research Laboratory, U.S. Environmental Protection Agency, Cincinnati, OH 45268

Of the approximately 10 million tons of toxic and hazardous wastes which are generated yearly in the United States, it has been estimated that 10 to 20% will need special methods for disposal because of extreme difficulties in their treatment. These materials are made up in large part from pesticides which have been withdrawn from use, obsolete or below-specification toxic substances, industrial wastes from chemicals, explosives, etc., and biological residues, carcinogens, mutagens, and related materials(1). They exist in multiple ton quantities, as well as small centigram batches at a multitude of locations throughout the United States. They are, specifically, materials in search of a disposal method, and include the following exceedingly dangerous compounds and mixtures:

o Cancer-causing nitrosamines, vinyl and vinylidene chlorides, dioxin-containing organohalogens, and aromatic amine compounds which heretofore have been considered only as oddities, or as being present only in small quantities

o Acute-toxicity organometallic compounds and heavy metal complexes, such as mercury, arsenic, cadmium, and lead compounds, derived from industrial processes and pesticides

o Nerve-poisons from military sources, which include organophosphorus chemicals stockpiled above ground, and from pesticide wastes which are only slightly less hazardous

All of these are problem materials which give great concern to those who are responsible for their safe disposal. Their identification and sources (2) are abstracted in Table I.

Current Disposal Techniques for Highly Toxic Materials

For compounds of nominal toxicity, such as diluted DDT or other pesticides mixed with solvent or municipal sludges, on the order of LD_{50}* of 500 or higher, notable achievements have been accomplished in thermal destruction, chemical and biological detoxification, and special landfill methods. However, with the exception of incinerator processing, relatively little new technol-

*Oral lethal dose for 50% of test animals in mg/kg of body weight.

Table I.   Identities and Known Sources of Highly Toxic and Hazardous Substances within Continental U.S.

Toxic Material	Classification	Source of Material	Quantities and Location, Where Known	Disposal Method
Organophosphorus Compounds:				
• Nerve gases or G-agents (phosphonofluoridates)	Anticholinesterase nerve toxin	Military: Stored pure agents. Stored waste streams. Stored neutralization products	Thousands of gallons; Several thousand lb (Colorado, Utah, Maryland)	Storage(b) above ground, " " " "
• Flame retardant (e.g., "Tris")	Carcinogen	Manufacturer	Probable 1000's of lb (California)	Unknown
• Pesticides (phosphonates, thiophosphonates)	Anticholinesterase	Commercial, Industrial, Agricultural: Pesticide manufacturing wastes; Outdated supplies; Unlabeled, unknown supplies	1 to 10,000 lb in various locations	Chemical disposal sites, Incineration
Organometallic Compounds:				
• Arsenical pesticides	Lipoid toxin	Commercial, Industrial, Agricultural: Solids; Holding ponds (Alexandria, Va. area) New Mexico)	100's of lb; 100 to 1000 gallons	Storage underground; Storage above ground
• Mercurials pesticides	Primary organ toxins in humans	Solids, solutions	100's of lb, gallons	Storage underground
• Lead (tetraethyl lead)	" " " "	Process wastes	1000's of lb (East and West Coast)	Storage above ground
• Metal cyanides	" " " "	Plating wastes, solids		Storage above and underground; Wet oxidation, UV, ozonolysis
• Nickel carbonyl, Zn, Cd, Mn, Se, V, Misc. Heavy metal compounds	Primary organ toxins	Petroleum catalysts, pesticides, experimental complexes	1 to 100 lb, a few 1000's of lb (Texas, California, New Jersey)	Storage above and underground
Halogenated Compounds:				
• Hexachlorobenzene (containing dioxin) PCBs, Kepone, Mirex, etc.	Carcinogens	Commercial, Agricultural	1000's of lb	Storage above and underground, Incineration
• DBCP (dibromochloropropane)	Male sterility in humans	Fumigant/agricultural chemicals	Estimated 1000's of lb (California)	Unknown
• Vinyl and vinylidene chlorides	Carcinogens	Industrial waste streams and process bottoms	Estimated 1000's of lb	Storage and incineration
Organonitrogen Compounds:				
• Nitrosamines (e.g., dimethyl nitrosamine)	Carcinogens, teratogens, mutagens	Industrial, Hospitals, Universities, Cancer Centers.	1 to 10 lb (throughout U.S.)	Storage above and below ground
• Aromatic amines (e.g., benzidines)	"	"	100's of lb	" " " "
• Polyaromatic hydrocarbons, PAH (dyes, pigments)	"	U.S. Navy smokes, flares, etc.	100's of lb	Unknown

(a) LD$_{50}$ < 100 (oral lethal dose 50% test animals, < 100 mg/1 kg body weight).
(b) Temporary method: Materials have not been rendered chemically or biologically safe.

ogy has been developed within the last 10 years for the disposal of highly toxic, refractory, and extremely persistent wastes in the form of concentrates, pure chemicals, or nondiluted process wastes.

Current methods have been almost exclusively underground landfill, or aboveground warehouse or exposed-drum storage. This is not a true disposal, but a "hiding" action, in that the materials are still there, in place, waiting for a method which will carry out the detoxification eventually. The substances will actually remain for future generations to be troubled with.

Preliminary Microwave Plasma Detoxification Studies

Research on the decomposition of organic compounds by passage through a microwave discharge began at the Lockheed Palo Alto Research Laboratory (LPARL) in 1967. Since it was well known that microwave discharges could be used to promote a variety of chemical reactions (3), it was considered reasonable that this approach could be applied to the scission or destruction of bonds in compounds which, for various reasons, were considered objectionable. In a U. S. Army-supported program conducted during 1970-1972, the decomposition of toxic gas simulants was carried out in discharges containing helium and air in which nearly 100% decomposition of selected organophosphonate materials was effected (4). The materials were passed through a small 1-5 g/hr capacity laboratory-size reactor, having a plasma volume of about 10 cm^3. For commercial or plant-scale development of the process, it was obvious that large-capacity reactors would be required. When it was determined that larger size microwave power applicators could be obtained on a custom basis from microwave hardware suppliers, the U. S. EPA, Solid and Hazardous Waste Research Division, Municipal Environmental Research Laboratory, Cincinnati, Ohio, supported the following study to test the process on several toxic pesticides and wastes.

Program Objectives

The primary objective of the program was evaluation of the effectiveness of an expanded scale microwave plasma system for processing hazardous organic compounds, wastes, and pesticides of current interest. The reaction products would also be identified to verify that the products were innocuous, and to assess the possibility for recovery of useful materials as by-products. The data presented below describes the chemistry of the reactions, the initial scale-up of microwave hardware, and an evaluation of the process in which 450 to 3200 grams (1 to 7 lb) per hr were decomposed to harmless or readily disposable effluents.

Microwave Plasma Characteristics

A plasma or discharge is a partially ionized gaseous mixture consisting of free electrons, ions, and various neutral species. The free electrons are the principal initiators of the plasma

reactions. When the electrons undergo inelastic collisions with
the reactants, they cause either ionization, which produces more
electrons and ions, or dissociation of the reactants into free
radicals. These fragments, with their unpaired electrons, can
then undergo a series of rapid reactions to the final products.
     The free electrons are energized by the oscillating electric
field produced by the microwave energy (2450 MHz) applied to the
gas.   In this way, the electrons couple the electrical energy
with the reactants and force them to undergo the desired reactions.
The oscillating electric field produced by the microwaves changes
polarity so rapidly that the charged species in the plasma reverse
their direction of acceleration before they are swept to the walls
where they are likely to be destroyed. Therefore, the plasma can
be maintained without the use of internal electrodes which are
usually required for plasmas operating at lower frequencies. Consequently, there is no problem with internal electrode decomposition from corrosive species in the plasma.
     The plasma used in these investigations is operated at re-
duced pressures up to a few hundred torr. This permits the free
electrons to be energized to temperatures much higher than that of
the neutral gases, since at these lower pressures there are many
less inelastic collisions occurring which would cool down the reactive electrons. The electron "temperatures" are well over
10,000°K (3), while the temperature of the neutral gas is less
than 1,000°K. By operating under these nonequilibrium conditions,
it is possible to maintain the free electrons at high temperatures
without heating the bulk neutral gas, thereby conserving electrical energy. Since the plasma decomposition mechanism is principally electronic, rather than thermal, the microwave applicator-
power coupling equipment can be maintained at relatively low temperatures. Thus, the materials of construction associated with
furnaces or incinerator equipment are generally unnecessary, and
maintenance expenses will be low. In addition, the systems are
leak tight, which is a result of the requirement for working at
reduced pressures, thereby contributing to a high level of safety
in operation. Reference 4 may be consulted for additional information on these characteristics.

EQUIPMENT AND MATERIALS

Microwave Plasma Systems
     Microwave plasmas were produced in a laboratory-size reson-
ant cavity, and by three dual-trough waveguide applicators. A
block diagram of the plasma system is shown in Figure 1, and applies to all systems irrespective of applicator type or power
source.
     The laboratory scale plasma was used during the initial
stages of the study to determine product identities and conversion efficiencies. The laboratory apparatus was essentially the
same as that utilized previously for the decomposition of organo-

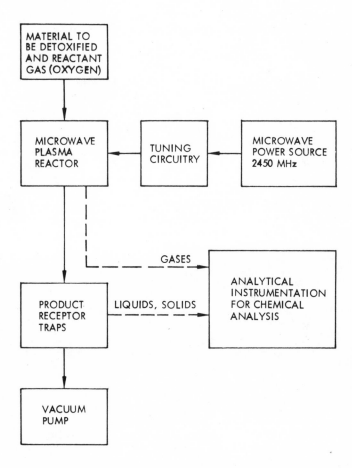

Figure 1. Block diagram of microwave plasma system and related components

phosphonate compounds, but required a modification in technique
for the dropwise introduction of liquids. A gravity-feed pressure-
equalized dropping funnel of approximately 100 cm^3 capacity was
installed at the input to the plasma reactor for this purpose. A
method was also required to increase the time for passage of the
drops through the discharge. This was necessitated since the time
of fall under vacuum through the plasma was too short, as
evidenced by drops exiting the reactor without having reacted completely. A solution to the problem was obtained by utilizing a
hollow quartz mesh "basket" positioned at the center of the plasma
zone. Quartz mesh fibers were loaded into the basket to serve as
a contact area for the drops. The basket contained a number of
holes to allow passage of the effluent products. The residence
time of the drops within the basket were estimated to be 1/2 to 1
sec, the time for reaction flashes to be completed in the plasma
zone.
     A schematic of the expanded scale plasma system is shown in
Figure 2. The microwave power applicator and power supply hardware were supplied by Gerling Moore, Inc., Palo Alto, CA. The
principal difference between the latter system and the laboratory
model involves the method of application of power to the reactor.
In the laboratory unit, the applicator was a resonant cavity,
Varian Associates, Model EC2DRS2, which was fed by a single 2.5-
kW 2450-MHz power supply. In the expanded scale unit, a dual-
trough waveguide applicator was used in which each trough was fed
by a 2.5-kW 2450-MHz power source. For additional information on
the applicators, Reference 5 may be **consulted**.
     In the expanded scale systems, the reactor tubes were fabri-
cated from transparent quartz of about 50 mm o.d., and 1.5-2.0 mm
wall thickness. Quartz Raschig rings and, in some instances,
quartz wool plugs were used to fill sections of the reactor to
increase the residence time within the plasma zone. The liquid
feed system was based on a 1-liter pressure-equalized version of
the unit used for the laboratory scale plasma tests. For relatively volatile solutions, however, atmospheric pressure was maintained above the solution to avoid vacuum pumping the solvent from
the solution. In this instance, a 250 cm^3 volumetric dropping
buret was used for feeding directly into the reactor.
     Reduced pressures were obtained using a Welch DuoSeal Model
1397 oil-sealed 2-stage mechanical pump with a free air displacement of 425 liters per min. Various cold trap configurations were
installed between the reactor output and the pump for product collection, and to maintain cleanliness of the pump oil. A photo-
graph of typical system components is shown in Figure 3.
     During the operation of the microwave units, a Holaday Model
HI 1500-3 microwave radiation monitor (Holaday Industries, Inc.,
Edina, Minnesota), and a Narda Model B86B3 radiation monitor
(Narda Microwave Corp., Plainview, N.Y.) were used to monitor
power leakage. Levels were less than 1 mW/cm^2 in the immediate
vicinity of the discharge tube.

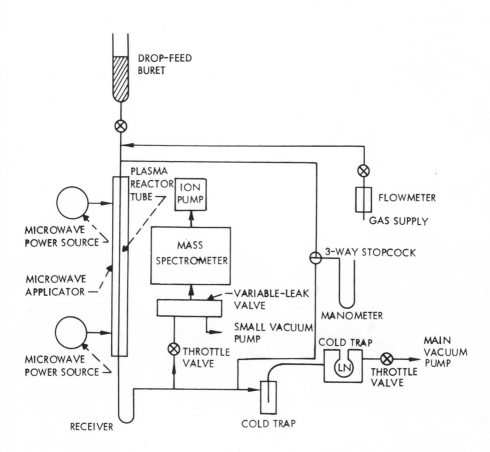

Figure 2. Schematic of expanded-scale microwave plasma system

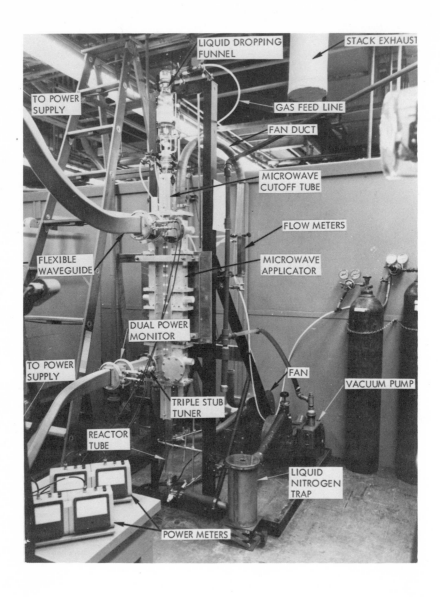

Figure 3.   Microwave plasma detoxification system

Analytical Systems

Mass spectrometric (MS) analysis of the gases leaving the reactor was performed on a Varian Associates Model 974-0002 residual gas analyzer (quadrupole mass spectrometer) with a range of
250 atomic mass units. A small quantity of the gas was continuously pumped past a variable-leak sampling valve. The gases bled
into the mass spectrometer by the sampling valve were pumped from
the system by an ion pump. The sampling system is included in
Figure 3. Infrared spectra of solid and liquid effluents collected
from the product receiver and traps were obtained on a Perkin-
Elmer 621 infrared spectrophotometer with a range of 4000 to 400
cm^{-1} (2.5 to 25 microns). Materials to be analyzed were ground
with KBr and compressed into pellets for scanning over the pre-
scribed spectrum.

Visible and ultraviolet spectra from 200 to 700 nm on solid
and liquid effluents were obtained on a Cary Model 14 Recording
Spectrophotometer using conventional procedures.

A Finnegan Model 4021 GC/MS Data System was used toward completion of the study for polyaromatic hydrocarbons.

Pesticides, Hazardous Wastes, and Gases

The materials which were detoxified or decomposed are listed
in Table II. Selections were made on the basis of the extent of
the environmental problems which were associated with these materials, EPA's interest, and the refractory characteristics of the
materials. The reactant/carrier gases were the following: oxygen, 99.5% min. purity, Fed. Spec. BB-0-925(a), Type I; argon,
99.995% min. purity, Mil-A-18455B. The oxygen contained 0.5%
maximum impurities, in which approximately 0.05% was nitrogen,
the remainder being argon and other gases in trace amounts.

EXPERIMENTAL PROCEDURE

In general, the procedure for operation of both laboratory
and expanded scale units was the same as that described in Reference 4. Certain modifications were required as the result of differences in feed technique, however. For example, when a vacuum
dropping funnel was used for introduction of a low volatility
fluid, the entire system, including the section above the liquid,
was evacuated to 1 torr. The pressure was then adjusted to about
10 torr by the addition of oxygen or argon. The microwave power
was then turned on to start the plasma. Additional gas was introduced to obtain the desired pressure and flow rate in combination
with regulation by the main throttle valve. The microwave power
was set to the desired level with the tuning controls adjusted
to give minimum reflected power. After obtaining a background MS
scan (reactant gas flowing minus material to be detoxified), a
needle valve at the bottom of the dropping funnel was opened to
yield the desired feed rate. The gaseous effluent from the plasma
was then sampled and analyzed by MS. For methyl bromide gas, the

Table II. Pesticides and Hazardous Wastes for Detoxification Tests

Classification	Material	Form Tested	Manufacturer or Source	Grade or Type
Organophosphorus Pesticide	Malathion (95% min. purity)	Pure Liquid	American Cyanamid	ULV
Chlorinated Hydrocarbon Waste	PCB's (Polychlorinated Biphenyls)	Liquid Mixture	Monsanto	Aroclor 1242 Aroclor 1254
Brominated Hydrocarbon Rodenticide	Methyl Bromide (99.5% min. purity)	Commercial Gas	Matheson Gas	—
Heavy Metal Fungicide	Phenylmercuric Acetate (30% PMA solids)	Commercial Aqueous Methanol Solution	Troy Chemical	Troysan PMA-30
Chlorinated Hydrocarbon Pesticide	Kepone (80% Active Ingredient, 20% Clay)	1. Commercial Powder 2. Laboratory Aqueous Dispersion 3. Laboratory Methanol Solution	Allied Chemical	80% Powder Concentrate, Technical Grade, Code 9406
Polyaromatic Red Dye Mixture	55.4% Xylene azo-β-naphthol 18.9% 1-Methylaminanthraquinone 18.0% Sucrose 1.8% Graphite 5.9% Silica Binder (KClO$_3$ oxidant excluded)	1. Laboratory Aqueous Dispersion 2. Laboratory Methyl Ethyl Ketone Solution	Naval Weapons Support Center Crane, Indiana	U.S. Navy MK 13 Mod O Marine Smoke and Illumination Signal

pesticide was fed directly, bypassing the funnel. Product traps were an ice water cooled receiver, followed by one or more liquid nitrogen (LN) or dry-ice acetone traps.

RESULTS

Laboratory Scale Plasma Reactor

Reactions in the laboratory system were carried out with the toxic substances mixed with oxygen or argon. Although it was well known that simpler organic compounds exposed to inert gas plasmas would react to form a variety of compounds, including polymers (6), nevertheless, argon, in addition to oxygen, was evaluated for comparison with the helium and air decomposition reactions previously reported. However, after observing, for example, the offensive mercaptan/sulfide compounds which resulted from the malathion-argon plasma reactions, the formation of carbonaceous flake deposites from methyl bromide-argon, plus assessing the probability for the formation of extremely toxic methyl mercury compounds from PMA and other organomercurials in argon (or other inert gases),emphasis was directed toward utilization of oxygen as the sole reactant gas for use in the expanded scale system. Details of the laboratory reactions which led to these conclusions are listed below.

Malathion-oxygen. Cythion ULV grade malathion was passed through a 200 to 250-W plasma at 100 to 120 torr using the quartz basket technique. The reactions appeared to occur spontaneously as the drops contacted the quartz fibers. With the exception of a white etch zone and a high viscosity water-white liquid that formed below the plasma zone, all the products were gases. Mass spectrometry indicated CO_2, CO, SO_2, and H_2O as effluent gases. Infrared spectroscopy showed the liquid product to be phosphoric acid. Material balances indicated that metaphosphoric acid was the probable material from which conversion to orthophosphoric acid in moist air occurred in 1 to 2 days. Analysis for malathion in the liquid reaction product was carried out spectrophotometrically in the visible region (7). Percent conversion was 99.98 + percent based on 0.016 percent malathion determined.

Polychlorinated biphenyl (PCB) - oxygen. Monsanto Aroclor 1242 liquid was passed through a 250-W plasma at 100 torr. Mass balance showed no liquids attributable to the starting material. All the products of decomposition were gases. On the basis of control runs in the absence of the plasma reaction, percent conversion was calculated at greater than 99.9 percent. Gas products were identified as CO_2, CO, H_2O, HCl, Cl_2, with minor amounts of Cl_2O and $COCl_2$. The latter gases, chlorine oxide and phosgene, were not observed in the expanded scale plasma reactions; instead, hydrogen chloride was the principal Cl-containing product.

Methyl bromide - oxygen. Gaseous methyl bromide was passed through a 300 to 400-W 50-torr oxygen plasma at 2 to 3 g/hr. The products of reaction were CO_2, CO, H_2O, HBr, and Br_2. Oxides of bromine were found in the liquid nitrogen traps, but were not otherwise observed at ambient temperatures. The extent of the reaction was determined by mass spectrometer, in which the ratios of the CH_3Br ion signal intensities before and during the plasma reactions were compared. Decomposition was greater than 99 percent, which was the limit of precision of the mass spectrometer for this chemical system.

Phenylmercuric acetate - oxygen. Commercial Troysan PMA-30 solution was passed through 225 to 280-W plasmas at 120 torr. Mercury metal was observed as a metallic mirror on the glass tubing downstream from the discharge zone. Material balance indicated >99.9% decomposition to the metal. Mass spectrometry showed the products formed in addition to Hg were H_2O, CO_2, and CO. There was no evidence of dimethyl mercury or other volatile organomercurials.

Malathion - argon. Decomposition reactions were carried out at 200-250 W, 100 torr, in pure argon. The resultant yellow-brown products were extremely offensive and malodorous, similar to mercaptan and disulfide compounds. Because of their potential for very high toxicity, further analysis was not undertaken.

Methyl bromide - argon. Methyl bromide was mixed with argon and passed through 300 to 400-W plasmas at 50 torr. The products of reaction estimated by mass spectrometer were Br_2, HBr, methane, ethylene, and acetylene. Carbonaceous flake deposits were formed in the reactor tube. Quantitative analysis by MS showed that not less than 99 percent conversion had occurred.

Expanded Scale Plasma Reactor

The approach taken in the study was to obtain maximum throughput, with the objective of achieving low process costs. Generally, the total microwave power available, 4.2 to 4.7 kW, was applied to the discharge. This allowed the plasma to operate at higher pressures, thereby permitting a maximum amount of oxygen to be used as the plasma gas for reaction with the pesticides and wastes.

During the initial runs, the Series A microwave power applicator with a 2.7 liter reactor vol. was used for plasma decompositions of Aroclor No. 1242 PCB. It was determined that the liquid had been decomposed and that one of the reaction products — a black soot-like deposit which coated the product receiver — contained little or no PCB, as determined by infrared spectroscopy. After additional runs were carried out in which feed, pressure, and absorbed power were varied, it became apparent that the reactor was too large in volume for the power available. Series B and C applicators, having reactor volumes 1.5 and 0.6 liters, respectively, were evaluated in turn. The results are detailed in Table III and are described in the following sections.

Malathion liquid was drop-fed onto a porous, quartz wool bundle positioned at the top power input to the plasma zone. By this means, in a mechanism similar to that which was used in the

Table III. Summary of Expanded-Scale Oxygen Plasma Reactions

Pesticide/Waste	Run No.	Applicator Series	Microwave Power (kW)	Feed Rate [g/hr (lb/hr)]	Pressure Range (torr)	Oxygen Gas Flow (liters/hr)	Reactor Packing(a)	Conversion (%)
Malathion "Cythion" ULV	31-16	B	3.7	504(1.1)	28-46	361	Wool Plug	99.9988
Malathion "Cythion" ULV	31-46	B	4.7	480(1.1)	28-30	480	Wool Plug	99.9999
PCB Aroclor 1242	31-8	B	4.6	270(0.6)	17-35	323	Wool Plug	>99
PCB Aroclor 1242	31-10	B	4.2	492(1.1)	19-36	395	Wool Plug	>99
PCB Aroclor 1254	31-62	B	4.5	206(0.4)	13-25	360	Solid Rings	>99
PMA Troysan PMA-30	31-88	C	4.6	1020(2.25)	120-140	960	Raschig Rings	Complete, estim. 99.99(b)
PMA Troysan PMA-30	31-108	C	4.0	2380(5.25)	100-120	792	Raschig Rings	Complete, estim. 99.99
PMA Troysan PMA-30	31-110	C	4.3	2950(6.5)	100-120	792	Raschig Rings	Complete, estim. 99.99
Kepone 80/20 20% Methanol Solution	38-30	C	4.6	(b)	45-60	720	Raschig Rings	>99(b)
Kepone 80/20 10% Solids, Aqueous Slurry	38-36	C	4.2	—	35-50	None	Raschig Rings	>99
Kepone 80/20 2- to 3-g Solid Discs	38-38	C	4.6	—	30-70	810	Raschig Rings	>99
Red Dye Mixture 15.5% Solids Aqueous Slurry	68-58	C	4.6	(b)	35-60	300	Raschig Rings	>99.9999

(a) Quartz
(b) See text.

Table IV. Effect of Packed Bed on PMA-30 (Phenylmercuric Acetate) Conversion in Series C Plasma System

| Run No. | Packing of 45-mm i.d. Reactor | | Oxygen Flow (Standard liter/min) | Pressure (torr) | | Microwave Power (kW) | Throughput (lb/hr) | Notes |
	Ring Size o.d. × Length (mm)	Bed Length (cm)		Top	Bottom			
31-88	8 × 8	16	8 to 16	120	90	4.6	2.25	Reactor filled approximately one-half with rings
31-108	8 × 8	45	13.2	120	64	4.0	5.25	Reactor completely filled with rings
31-110	8 × 8	45	13.2	120	60	4.3	6.5	Repeat of 31-108
38-6	10 × 10	34	13.2	115	42	4.3	4.25	Largest rings in series
38-8	8 × 4	31	13.2 to 18.4	112	60	4.6	6.0	Smallest rings in series
38-14	8 × 8	31	13.2 to 16.0	130	75	4.7	8.0	CH_3OH component observed at 8 lb/hr

laboratory-scale system, large numbers of smaller droplets were produced within the matrix of the wool, and propelled by the gas stream through the plasma. Products were S, SO_2, CO_2, CO, and H_2O, plus a liquid phosphoric acid. During the reaction, deposits of a dark yellow-brown sulfur product mixed with a clear water-white high viscosity liquid were formed which flowed slowly down the sides of the reactor into the receiver. No carbonaceous or other products resembling the starting material were observed. Spectrophotometric analysis of the liquids from the two reactions gave residues of 12 ppm and 1 ppm malathion.

Polychlorinated biphenyls (PCB's) yielded HCl, CO_2, CO, and H_2O as determined by MS. No Cl_2O or $COCl_2$ was observed. There was formation of some soot in the product receiver; infrared analysis gave no indication of PCB residues. It was determined, however, that at throughput levels of about 1 kg (2 lb) per hr in the B applicator system, complete reaction had not occurred. This was determined by infrared analysis of the black tar-like liquid products in the receiver trap which indicated the presence of PCB starting material. Consequently, the Series C applicator was tested next to determine its usefulness for increasing the level of throughput.

Phenylmercuric acetate, Troysan PMA-30 solution, was passed through the Series C system in several runs to determine the effect of the shortened length of the applicator, as well as to determine the effect of quartz plugs and rings in the reactor tube. The reaction was considered complete if none of the methanol component was found by mass spectrometry in the effluent gas. Mass spectrometer sensitivity was 2 to 3 parts per thousand for methanol, based on control runs performed in the absence of the plasma. The MS analysis showed that at a throughput of 3600 g (8 lb) per hr, small amounts of methanol were detected in the effluent. This indicated that maximum detoxification or destruction of PMA-30 would occur at about 7 lbs/hr. The principal gases of the reaction were CO_2, CO, and H_2O. Volatile organomercurials were not detected by MS. Metallic mercury was deposited in the traps downstream from the plasma.

Experiments were performed to modify the residence time of the feed materials in the plasma zone. Quartz Raschig rings were tested to evaluate throughput under different packed bed conditions. For PMA-30, maximum throughput was defined as the feed rate which showed no methanol component in the plasma effluent as determined by mass spectrometer.

For the Kepone runs, a commercial mixture, Allied Chemical 80% powder concentrate, was used as a starting material. Approximately 200 g was converted into aqueous slurries, methanol solutions, and presscakes. The solid presscakes were prepared by compressing 2-3 g batches in a die under 1,000 psi pressure. The discs, which required a strong finger pressure to fracture, were placed at the top of the Raschig ring area in the plasma reactor tube before the plasma was initiated. It was observed visually that breakdown and decomposition of the solids occurred within 10 to 30 seconds, depending on the flow of oxygen and the pressure within the reactor. Solutions of 20% Kepone-methanol after filtration to remove the clay particles, were gravity fed into the plasma from a 250 cm^3 buret needle-valve feed system in which atmospheric pressure instead of reduced pressure was maintained over the solution. Dispersions of Kepone formed readily and were fed unfiltered from the same system. The gaseous reaction products from the solvent and slurry mixtures were CO_2, CO, HCl, and H_2O; phosgene or chlorinated hydrocarbons were not detected by MS.

Because of the short 10 to 30-sec reaction times for the solid Kepone presscakes, mass spectrometric analysis of the gaseous effluents were not performed. Instead, the clay support powders which passed through the reactor were collected from the receiver and analyzed by infrared spectroscopy. No Kepone or hexachlorobenzene was detected in the solid residues. Percentage conversions were estimated at better than 99%. Because of the limited quantity of the starting material, the reactions were not maximized with respect to throughput.

A polyaromatic dye composition comprised of two polyaromatic dyes, sucrose, carbon black, and silica, which make up U. S. Navy MK 13 Mod 0 Marine Smoke and Illumination Signal, was introduced into the plasma as a solvent solution and as an aqueous dispersion. The dye components were 55.4% xylene azo-β-naphthol and 18.9% 1-methylaminoanthraquinone. The $KClO_3$ oxidant was omitted from the evaluation in this series. For the dye-solvent solution, a 15% solids methyl ethyl ketone (MEK) mixture was decomposed. After the reaction, there were no red colorations or residues visible below the reactor. However, because the MEK oxygen demand would prevent development of a high throughput, an aqueous vehicle was tested for use as part of the feed system. Also, since the red dye components as a mixture were essentially hydrophobic, an ethylene oxide nonylphenol surfactant, TEC 1216E (TEC Chemical Co., Monterey Park, CA) was utilized to yield after filtration, a 15.5% hydrophilic slurry, density 1.03 g/cm^3. The slurry was added at rates from 2 to 8 cm^3/min. The reactions were not maximized because of limitations in starting material supply, as was the case for Kepone. Based on wt%, the solid residue measured less than 0.2% in the receiver traps, or >99.8% conversion to gaseous products.

Based on wt% of starting material, less than 0.2% solid residue passed through the reactor, or 99.8% conversion to gaseous products. Spectrophotometric comparisons in the visible region of a methylene dichloride solution of the unknown solid, and known concentrations of the initial dye mixture in the same solvent indicated that not more than 5 ppm of the dyes had passed through the plasma. Polyaromatic hydrocarbons were not detected above 2 ppm using UV fluorescence, infrared and UV absorption spectrophotometry, and GC/MS. The <0.2% reddish-brown residue showed via IR absorption and GC/MS, the additional presence of dioctyl-

phthalate, silicones, and benzene traces which probably entered
the analytical samples during the CH_2Cl_2 washing of the traps and
connective tubing.

DISCUSSION

Chemistry of Plasma Decomposition Reactions
    In general, the decomposition of organic materials, such as
pesticides, chlorinated wastes, etc., will encompass a large number of complex reactions. The primary step in each instance involves collisions between the compound and either free electrons
or reactive species produced by the action of the discharge on the
reactant gas. Through the action of electron collisions with
other species, free radicals and atoms are produced from the organic compounds. These species then react further to form second-
ary products.
    When oxygen is utilized as the reactant gas in the plasma,
atomic oxygen becomes the primary reactive species which rapidly
oxidizes the organic compounds introduced into the discharge. In
addition, the large numbers of energetic free electrons continually
bombard the compounds, and any remaining organic components will be
broken up into smaller free radical fragments, which rapidly react
with the oxygen present. The free electrons may also collide with
the CO_2 produced resulting in dissociation to CO and oxygen atoms
(8). The carbon monoxide can react with other oxygen species to
reform the carbon dioxide. Thus, an equilibrium concentration of
CO and CO_2 may be present under conditions of complete oxidative
conversion.
    In the malathion-oxygen reaction, complete oxidation appears
to have occurred in the laboratory system yielding colorless gases,
SO_2, CO_2, CO, and H_2O and metaphosphoric acid. In the Series B
reactor, there was no significant difference in efficiency, except
for the formation of some yellow, incompletely converted, sulfur-
like solids. Disappearance of the solids would be expected in the
Series C reactor, with its improved packing, resulting in an increase in SO_2, H_2O, etc.
    For PCB-oxygen, reactions in the laboratory system yielded
Cl_2, HCl, CO_2, CO, H_2O, minor amounts of Cl_2O and $COCl_2$, and a
soot-like product in the receiver. It appears probably that the
Cl_2O (9) and/or Cl_2 (10) reacted with some of the CO to produce
the observed $COCl$. In the expanded scale Series B reactor, no
Cl_2O or $COCl_2$ was observed, which may have resulted from the dif-
fering reactor conditions. Further optimization in the Series C
system should result in the disappearance of the soot, and formation of increased amounts of HCl, CO_2, CO, and H_2O.
    With regard to the observed differences in throughput of the
Series B and C reactors, the variations may be related to the
power densities which differ for each reactor. The B reactor,
with a volume of 1.5 liters, exclusive of packing, produced a maximum power density of 3.1 watts/cm^3, as calculated from run 31-46,

whereas the C reactor, with a 0.6 liter volume, developed 7.1 watts/cm^3 in run 31-110. The greater power per unit volume in the latter system would result in additional capacity for maintaining the oxygen discharge at increased pressures, thereby permitting greater quantities of organic compounds to be decomposed within the plasma.

In the laboratory detoxification of methyl bromide, in addition to CO_2, CO, H_2O, HBr, and Br_2, minor amounts of yellow-brown products, probably BrO_2 and/or Br_2O, were observed in the LN traps. The bromine oxides are not stable at room temperature (11) and would be found only in reactor systems that utilize this type of trap.

For phenylmercuric acetate-oxygen, the formation of metallic mercury in both laboratory and expanded scale reactors may be explained by postulating HgO as an intermediate in the plasma reaction, followed by its decomposition or dissociation between 440° and 610°C (12). Oxidation of the methanol solvent would be expected to follow the usual mechanism to CO_2, CO, and H_2O.

For Kepone-oxygen, the plasma reaction products of 20% Kepone-methanol solutions in the expanded scale system yielded oxides of carbon, water, and hydrochloric acid, and may be considered to have been completely oxidized. Reactions of Cl_2, produced from the oxidation of the Kepone molecule, would be expected to react with the H_2O derived from the oxidation of methanol, resulting in HCl and HClO; the latter, being unstable, would decompose to HCl and oxygen. In an experiment which involved a Kepone slurry exposed to the discharge in the absence of an oxygen flow, the resultant successful conversion of the pesticide can be related to the formation of, and subsequent reaction with, a water or steam plasma (13) derived from the aqueous component of the mixture. In both plasma reactions, the products were essentially the same.

For the polyaromatic dye-oxygen system, the components of the mixture reacted to form gases and <0.2% solid residue. Very little, if any, dye starting materials and no significant polyaromatic hydrocarbons (PAH) were detected. Since PAH has been found in air oxidation products derived from these materials (14), a significant advantage would appear to derive from the discharge process.

Differences in oxygen demand can be expected for the various pesticides and wastes as the result of differences in molecular composition, related principally to the number of hydrogen atoms in the molecule. For example, Kepone, $C_{10}Cl_{10}O$, will require significantly less oxygen than PCB, Aroclor 1254, average composition $C_{12}H_5Cl_5$, for conversion to CO_2 and CO. Also, the use of solvents, such as MEK, as vehicles to transport the pesticides into the plasma, will result in consumption of significant amounts of oxygen. Therefore, unless solvents are part of the original mixture to be detoxified, the addition of these materials for reasons of convenience in feed or handling will be detrimental to the overall throughput.

When malathion or methyl bromide reacted in an argon plasma, the products were similar to those observed in the earlier gas reactions. Some of the sulfur in malathion, for example, appeared to form organic mercaptans or sulfides, rather than simple molecules, such as H_2S or SO_2. Thus, when argon is used as a carrier gas, the wide range of possible products would preclude the formation of compounds of low toxicity on a consistent basis. However, in an oxygen plasma, the resultant complete oxidation does permit an accurate prediction of the product stream and its level of toxicity.

Process Costs Calculated for PMA-30

For reactions in the expanded scale system, electrical power and oxygen costs were determined for 3 runs of increasing throughput. Electrical consumption was measured using a single 208-volt wattmeter through which all electrical equipment was routed. The data are presented in Table V. At 6.5 lb/hr, as detailed in run no. 31-110, approximately $0.08/lb for total oxygen and electrical costs was calculated.

For the determination of process costs for projected future 50 to 100 lb/hr plasma systems, an accurate assessment is difficult. However, where the object is to show the economic viability of the approach, it is possible to calculate values which can be derived from known process variables, and estimated oxygen, electrical, and related costs.

The material chosen for the calculation was phenylmercuric acetate (PMA); first, because it was considered refractory or difficult to decompose safely and completely and, second, because it had the potential for recovery of the mercury values in the metallic state.

The following assumptions are listed as part of the estimated costs.

Capital costs:	$100,000 per unit, 2 units in use
Electrical costs:	$0.015 kWh, industrial rate
Liquid oxygen costs:	$0.005/SCF, large volume usage
	Add $3,000/hr, storage fee.
Labor costs:	$9/hr, one-man operation of two automated units
Credit for metallic mercury	$1.50/lb

A standard 330-day/yr, 3-shift operation is used. Throughput is 50 lb/hr per unit, or 792,000 lb/yr. The process variables related to PMA-30 on a per-pound basis were for oxygen, 4.3 SCF, and electric line power, 1.6 kWh, obtained from run no. 31-110, which was the highest complete reaction throughput determined experimentally. The calculated costs are as follows:

Table V. Electrical and Oxygen Costs for PMA-30 Oxygen Plasma Reactions

Run No.	Microwave Power (kW)	Feed Rate [g/hr (lb/hr)]	Oxygen Flow [Std liter/hr (SCFH)]	Gas Cost[a] ($/lb)	Electrical Energy Consumed (kWh/lb)	Electrical Energy[b] Cost ($/lb)	Total Cost ($/lb)
31-88	4.6	1020(2.25)	960(34)	0.18	4.7	0.094	0.27
31-108	4.0	2380(5.25)	792(28)	0.064	1.9	0.038	0.10
31-110	4.3	2950(6.5)	792(28)	0.052	1.6	0.032	0.08

(a) O$_2$, $0.012/SCF
(b) Electrical, $0.02/kWh, industrial rate

Variable Costs

Operating Labor	$71,280
Oxygen	20,028
Electricity	19,008
Maintenance (4% of Investment)	8,000

Fixed Costs

Capital Recovery (10 yr-7%)	28,480
Taxes and Insurance (2%)	4,000

Total Annual Costs	150,796
Cost per Pound Treated	$0.19

Based on recovery and sale of the metallic mercury, a net profit of $0.085/lb is derived.

Process Development

As the result of accomplishments in the initial scaleup, the design and construction of higher capacity equipment and components has been continued. This includes positive displacement feed techniques for solids as well as liquids and slurries, additional microwave power, up to 15 kW, to generate an estimated throughput of 10 to 30 lbs/hr, and a high-power applicator for transfer of the increased microwave energy to the reactor tube. Cooling traps are required, especially for product separation and condensation. Based in part on its compatibility with wet gases, a water ring seal vacuum pump system has been designed. Analytical instrumentation has been extended to include an automatic gas chromatographic mass spectrometer-data system for detection of traces of potentially toxic materials in the ppm range. As part of the evaluation, data will be collected on electrical power and oxygen consumed, percent conversion, and mass throughput for oxygen plasma systems. These will be obtained in order to prepare an economic comparison between the microwave plasma process, incineration, and other conventional technologies.

Future Utilization

The microwave plasma system, as now envisioned, will be portable to, or may be situated at, sites where highly toxic materials are consumed, stored, or manufactured, including hospitals, universities, research facilities, agricultural stations, as well as chemical and industrial areas. The pesticides and hazardous wastes which can be treated by microwave plasma processing include gases, pure organic liquids, solutions, slurries, pure solids, and solids mixed with inorganic components. These are stored in drums, cannisters, bottles, in dispersion, and in settled-out form, both pumpable and in difficult-to-pump consistency, and therefore cover the full range of materials and materials handling technologies. Relative to large incinerator equipment, such as on the ship Vulcanus, the microwave system is, of course, small. It should be

noted, however, that transportation of hazardous wastes across
state lines may involve legal, political, and scientific questions
which have yet to be resolved.

CONCLUSIONS

Microwave plasma technology has been shown to be highly effective for the detoxification/destruction of hazardous organic
wastes. Toxic compounds and wastes of current interest were decomposed, and the reaction products identified to estimate their
toxicity, and to determine the potential for recovery of useful
materials. The study resulted in an expansion from 1 - 5 g up to
3 kg (7 lb) per hr in throughput.
With regard to oxygen plasma reactions in the expanded scale
system, the products were generally predictable, and no unexpected
toxic by-products were formed which could not be treated with
caustic. Of the systems to which high sensitivity analytical
techniques were applied, e.g., malathion and polyaromatic dyes,
very little or no starting material was detected in the residues,
and no significant toxic/carcinogenic substances were found in the
effluents. The potential for resource recovery was demonstrated
for a phenylmercuric acetate pesticide which yielded metallic mercury as a salable product. The process may permit the recovery of
chemical feedstocks when applied to other organometallic pesticides or wastes, which would otherwise be permanently lost. In
the future, utilizing higher power for the reactor, scaleup to a
pilot level throughput of 10 to 30 lbs/hr will be tested. Further
expansion to 50 - 100 lbs/hr is envisioned as feasible with current technology.

ABSTRACT

Detoxification of pesticides and hazardous wastes has been
performed successfully in a microwave-induced oxygen plasma. Materials were passed through a laboratory-size reactor to determine
conversion efficiencies and product identities. Construction of
an expanded-volume system followed which resulted in an increase
in throughput from 1 - 5 g/hr for the laboratory unit to 450 -
3200 g (1 to 7 lb) per hr in the larger system. Substances treated were PCB's, phenylmercuric acetate (PMA) solution, methyl bromide, malathion, a polyaromatic dye mixture, and Kepone. Detoxification of PMA yielded metallic mercury as a salable by-product.
Treatment costs were computed which included electricity, oxygen,
capital equipment, and labor.

ACKNOWLEDGMENT

The work upon which this publication is based was performed
pursuant to Contract 68-03-2190 with the U. S. Environmental Protection Agency, Cincinnati, Ohio. Additional support was obtained
from the Lockheed Independent Research Program. Appreciation is
tendered to Dr. Ernest L. Littauer, Lockheed Palo Alto Research
Laboratory, and Professor Alexis T. Bell, University of California,
Berkeley, for guidance and many valuable suggestions.

LITERATURE CITED

1. "Disposal of Hazardous Wastes," U.S. Environmental Protection
   Agency, Report to Congress, Publication SW-115, 1974.

2. Bailin, L. J., "Microwave Plasma Detoxification Process for
   Hazardous Wastes, Phase II, Systems Application Evaluation,"
   Lockheed Missiles & Space Company, Inc., Contract EPA 68-03-
   2190, Cincinnati, Ohio, October 1977.

3. McTaggart, F. K., "Plasma Chemistry in Chemical Discharges,"
   Elsevier, New York, 1967.

4. Bailin, Lionel J., Sibert, Merle E., Jonas, Lonard A., and
   Bell, Alexis T., "Microwave Decomposition of Toxic Vapor Simulants," Envir. Sci. & Technology, 9(3), 254-258 (1975).

5. Bailin, L. J. and Hertzler, Barry L., "Development of Micro-
   wave Plasma Detoxification Process for Hazardous Wastes,
   Phase I," Lockheed Missiles & Space Company, Inc., Contract
   EPA 68-03-2190, Final Report, U. S. EPA-600/2-77-030, Apr 77.

6. Millard, M., "Synthesis of Organic Polymer Films in Plasmas,"
   Chapter 5, "Techniques and Application of Plasma Chemistry,"
   Hollahan, John R., and Bell, Alexis T., Eds. 192-193, John
   Wiley, New York, 1975

7. Norris, M. V., Vail, W. A., and Averill, P. R., "Colorimetric
   Estimation of Malathion Residues," Agricultural and Food
   Chemistry., 2(11), 570-573 (1954).

8. Brown, Lloyd C. and Bell, Alexis T., "Kinetics of the Oxidation of Carbon Monoxide and the Decomposition of Carbon Dioxide in a Radiofrequency Electric Discharge," Ind. Eng. Chem.
   Fund, 13(3), 203-218 (1974).

9. Renard, J. J. and Boker, H. I., "Chemistry of Chlorine Monoxide," Chem. Rev., 76, 487-508 (1976).

10. Remy, H., "Treatise of Inorganic Chemistry," I, 449, Elsevier, Amsterdam, 1956.

11. Ibid., 810.

12. Ibid., II, 464.

13. Kaufman, F., "Production of Atoms and Simple Radicals in Glow Discharges," in "Chemical Reactions in Electrical Discharges," Advances in Chemistry Series No. 80, 45-46, American Chemical Society, Washington, D. C., 1969.

14. Owens, E. J., and Ward, D. M., "A Review of the Toxicology of Colored Chemical Smokes and Colored Smoke Dyes, EB-TR-74064, Edgewood Arsenal, Aberdeen Proving Ground, MD, Dec. 1964; available as DDC-AD-A003827.

MARCH 24, 1978

6

State of the Art Report on Pesticide Disposal Research[1]

RALPH R. WILKINSON, EDWARD W. LAWLESS, ALFRED F. MEINERS,
THOMAS L. FERGUSON, GARY L. KELSO, and FRED C. HOPKINS

Midwest Research Institute, 425 Volker Boulevard, Kansas City, MO 64110

The goal of this study is to review all published and other
available information on the current status of pesticide disposal
research with emphasis on high temperature incineration, physical-
chemical methods, and bioconversion technology. This paper is
being presented in order to acquaint you with our contract and
its preliminary findings, and to make contact with knowledgeable
persons in this field to obtain additional information. The
views expressed in this paper are those of the authors and do not
necessarily reflect the views or policies of the U.S. Environmental Protection Agency (EPA). We defer in-depth discussions of
Molten Salt Technology, Microwave Detoxification, Thermal Degradation, Photochemical Processes, and Catalytic Hydrodechlorination since these topics are covered by other participants at
this symposium.

High Temperature Incineration

The most recent investigations of the incineration of pesticides include studies of several classes of compounds and of
formulations as well as of pure active ingredients.

In a study by Midwest Research Institute (MRI) (1975), it
was concluded that organic pesticides may be destroyed with efficiencies approaching 99.999%. EPA recommended conditions for
incineration are 2 sec retention time at 1000°C. Other time-
temperature combinations are possible; e.g., 1 sec at 1100°C.
Excess air is required; 80 to 160% excess is recommended (Carnes
and Oberacker, 1976; Ferguson et al., 1975.)

1   This study was sponsored by the Environmental Protection
    Agency, Municipal Environmental Research Laboratory,
    Cincinnati, Ohio, under Contract No. 68-03-2527. Mr. Donald
    A. Oberacker was the Project Officer.

Environmentally hazardous emissions which must be controlled are particulate P_2O_5 and gaseous HCN, HCl, SO_2, and NO_x.
Recently, incineration of Kepone[R] and Mirex has been investigated by the University of Dayton Research Institute (UDRI) (1976) and by Midland-Ross Corporation (1977). A laboratory scale study by UDRI indicated that Kepone[R] decomposed at 500°C in 1 sec and Mirex at 700°C in 1 sec. The degree of efficiency was 99.998%. Both Kepone[R] and Mirex produce intermediate degradation products that are hazardous. For example, incineration of Kepone[R] can produce hexachlorocyclopentadiene, hexachlorobenzene, and an unidentified species (Carnes, 1977a; Duvall and Rubey, 1976).

The Midland-Ross Corporation incinerated small amounts of Kepone[R] (4 kg max. sample size) from January through March 1977. A total of 68 kg was destroyed. The incineration temperature was 1100°C. Retention time was reported as 2 sec. Major decomposition products were CO_2, H_2O, and HCl with traces of hexachlorobenzene. The draft report is not yet available (Carnes, 1977b).

The State of Virginia recently authorized Flood and Associates of Jacksonville, Florida, to design an incinerator to destroy 45,000 kg of Kepone[R]. The design will utilize the Midland-Ross Corporation data base.

Incineration at sea of organochlorine process wastes is being conducted by Shell Chemical Company in facilities in the Gulf of Mexico under an EPA permit. Although the wastes are not pesticides, the information gained and technology employed are directly applicable. Organochlorine wastes were incinerated at the rate of 25 metric tons/hr at 1200 to 1350°C average flame temperature. Efficiencies approached 99.9%. Emissions were essentially HCl, CO_2, and H_2O and were discharged directly to the atmosphere without scrubbing. Marine monitoring surveys below the effluent plume indicated no measurable increase in organochlorines in the water or in marine life (Wastler et al., 1975). Shell Chemical Company is currently operating under a 2-1/2 year special permit to burn 50,000 metric tons of chemical wastes (Environmental Sciences and Technology, 1977).

Incineration of 8.7 million liters of Herbicide Orange containing traces of the dioxin, TCDD, was accomplished during August of this year by the Dutch incinerator ship M/T Vulcanus in the mid-Pacific Ocean approximately 120 miles from Johnston Island and 1,000 miles west of the Hawaiian Islands. The U.S. EPA permit issued to the U.S. Air Force and Ocean Combustion Services, B.V. required at least 99.9% combustion efficiency.

Preliminary results of the incineration indicated·a greater than
99.99% combustion efficiency. No detectable TCDD was found in
the incinerator stack samples. The cost of the program was
around $5 million (Kansas City Times, 1977; Chemical and Engi-
neering News, 1977; Pesticide and Toxic Chemical News, 1977).

In summary, incineration has been shown to be highly efficient (99.9%), but capital investment can be great. Scrubbers
are normally required, although they are not if incineration is
performed at sea. Many classes of pesticides and their formulations have been examined. However, pilot plant scale demonstrations have not been conducted for several classes of pesticides
including anilides, ureas, uracils, and nitrated hydrocarbons.
Other classes of pesticides have been examined by only one or two
investigating teams. The data base for incineration of pesticides
must be expanded.

Chemical Treatment Processes

Many chemical approaches have been taken to detoxify or
destroy hazardous materials, including pesticides. These approaches generally involve rather simple treatment in solution
with alkali, acids, chlorine, oxygen, or hypochlorite, but may
include application of heat and pressure. Some of these methods
are capable of destroying pesticides, e.g., alkaline hydrolysis
of organophosphate compounds. Others only partially degrade the
active ingredient and yield products which are nearly as toxic
or even more toxic than the original pesticide. We shall mention only a few of these examples and indicate their general
usefulness, inherent shortcomings, and current status.

Wet Oxidation (Zimmerman Process, Zimpro®)--The principle
of operation is that a solution of any organic compound can be
oxidized by air or oxygen if sufficient heat and pressure is
applied. Thus, at temperatures of 150 to 340°C and 450 to 2,500
psig, sewage sludges will be oxidized to CO_2 and H_2O in 30 to
60 min. Sulfur, nitrogen, and phosphorus may remain in solution
as salts. Heavy metals may be precipitated as sulfates, phos-
phates, oxides, or hydroxides, or may remain in solution (Astro,
1977a).

The extent of actual pesticide destruction has rarely been
determined; the percent reduction in total organic carbon (TOC)
is given instead. For example, studies on DDT, 2,4-D, and pentachlorophenol (PCP) have been reported in this manner (Astro,
1977a). Other studies of the wet oxidation process applied to
Amiben® herbicide process wastes indicate 88 to 99.5% destruction

of the active ingredient (Astro, 1977b; Adams et al., 1976).
Atrazine process wastes have been claimed to be 100% destroyed
(Astro, 1977b).

Wet oxidation costs for processing 160,000 liters of chemical
waste per day have been estimated at $0.37/kg of active ingredient
destroyed and a capital investment of $2.2 million (Adams et al.,
1976).

Wet oxidation has not been demonstrated to be widely applicable to pesticides. This is primarily true because of the
lack of quantitative analytical data for the active ingredients;
merely monitoring the TOC reduction is inadequate. Secondly,
only two classes of pesticides have been examined: chlorinated
hydrocarbons and triazines. Much information on potential pesticide disposal applications for wet oxidation is yet to be developed.

Chlorolysis--Exhaustive chlorination as a method of disposing of pesticides and other chemical wastes has been suggested
at least since 1974 in the chemical press (Environmental Science
and Technology, 1974). Two U.S. patents describing basic im-
provements in chlorination appeared in 1972 (Krekeler et al.,
1972a,b). A recent study for the EPA--Industrial Environmental
Research Laboratory, Research Triangle Park--has assessed the
potential usefulness and economics of chlorolysis to destroy
pesticides and other chlorohydrocarbon wastes (Shiver, 1976). A
follow-up report, including process details and engineering cost
estimates, is currently in the draft stage (Des Rosiers, 1977).

Depending on the type of feedstock (aliphatic or aromatic)
exhaustive chlorination takes place over a range of pressures
and temperatures. According to a new process developed by
Farbwerke Hoechst AG, Frankfurt/Main, Germany, hydrocarbons and
their oxygenated or chlorinated derivatives are completely converted to CCl_4, $COCl_2$, and HCl at pressures up to 240 at. and
temperatures up to 620°C (Krekeler et al., 1975).

Pesticides and organic wastes that contain sulfur, nitrogen,
and/or phosphorus may have adverse effects on the chlorolysis
process. Thus, the presence of sulfur-bearing pesticides in
excess of 25 ppm sulfur in the hydrocarbon feedstream may cause
severe corrosion of the nickel tube catalytic reactor (Shiver,
1976). There is some question as to whether NCl_3 and PCl_3 or
PCl_5 would be formed in applying the chlorolysis process to N-
and P-containing pesticides, and of the hazards if these products were formed. Further research needs to be performed to
obtain information on these points.

We do not recommend chlorolysis for the disposal of organometallic pesticides without careful investigation and control;
some of the toxic heavy metals (e.g., As and Hg) would form volatile chlorides.

At least one cost estimate for a chlorolysis plant has been
made. A plant capacity to process 22,700 metric tons per year of
waste hydrocarbons or chlorohydrocarbons could yield from 5 to 14%
return on investment. Salable products are CCl_4, $COCl_2$, and HCl.
The capital investment for primary and auxiliary facilities may
be as high as $40 to $45 million. The cost to destroy the chlorohydrocarbon may be as high as $0.97/kg (Shiver, 1976).

On the basis of limited demonstrations of chlorolysis of
pesticides we can only indicate potential application to pesticides. Recently cancelled or greatly restricted pesticides are
those in the highly chlorinated category and those based on diene-
structures. Fortunately, these are the best candidates for chlorolysis.

Ozone/Ultraviolet (UV) Irradiation--Houston Research, Inc.,
has developed a method of destroying or detoxifying hazardous
chemicals in solution, including heavy metal cyanides and pesticides, utilizing a combination of ozonation and UV irradiation.
The technique involves rather simple apparatus: a reactor vessel,
an ozone generator, a gas diffuser or sparger, a mixer, and a
high-pressure mercury-vapor lamp. Pesticides that have been reduced to levels of < 0.5 ppm from an initial solution concentration of ~ 50 ppm include: PCP, malathion, Vapam® and Baygon®.
DDT has been reduced from 58 ppb in solution to < 0.5 ppb in 90
min (Mauk et al., 1976).

To date only two reactors, 10 and 21 liter volumes, have been
tested; both are considered to be bench-scale models. Houston
Research, Inc., indicates, however, that scale-up to much larger
sizes should be readily accomplished.

Only three classes of pesticides have been systematically
investigated using destruction by ozonation/UV irradiation:
chlorinated hydrocarbons (DDT and PCP); organophosphate compounds
(malathion); and, carbamates (Baygon® and Vapam®). For each of
these pesticides the experimental parameters have been optimized
to yield "complete destruction," i.e., 99+%, in the shortest
possible time. Thus, solution temperature, intensity of irradiation, ozonation flux, and stirring rate are all important
experimental parameters. Other pesticide classes have not been
investigated by this process to the best of our knowledge.

No cost estimates are available for this process. Principal capital equipment costs include the reactor, the ozone generator, power supply and controls, and the UV illumination source and power supply. Principal operating costs include electrical energy and labor.

Biodetoxification of Pesticides

Much of the research to date on pesticide biodegradation has focused on loss of desired toxicity under agricultural application and runoff conditions. Little of this work provides valuable carry-over in the realm of pesticide disposal. The large number of variables involved in microbial breakdown tends to make each research approach and result rather unique.

Some very important laboratory scale work has been performed by Dr. Douglas Münnecke, formerly with the EPA, now in West Germany (Münnecke, 1977; Münnecke and Hsieh, 1975). Emulsifiable parathion was the sole carbon and energy source for a mixed bacterial culture grown from sewage, soil, and water samples. After a 36-day adaptation period, the culture exhibited maximum growth in a solution containing 5,000 ppm parathion and showed only a slight decrease in activity when the parathion concentration was raised to 10,000 ppm. This higher level represents an approximation of the concentrations present in wash solutions from pesticide containers and aircraft spray tanks (Hsieh et al., 1972). Three different biochemical pathways were used by the culture to attack the emulsifiable parathion under aerobic or low oxygen conditions. The active organisms included five subclasses of fluorescent pseudomonads, plus species of Brevibacterium, Azotomonas, and Xanthomonas. The maximum concentration rate of degradation was 50 mg parathion per liter per hr.

The success of the culture was, in part, because of the production of the enzyme, parathion hydrolase. This enzyme was separated from the active cells and found to be tolerant of high temperatures (55°C for 10 min without deactivation) and suitable for substrate induction. The bacterial mixed culture demonstrated the ability to hydrolyze seven of eight tested organophosphate insecticides. Only Lebaycid®, with three different functional groups, was not hydrolyzed. Depending on the pesticide, biochemical detoxification rates when using 20 mg protein/liter, were 1 to 300 times faster than in chemical detoxification procedures using 0.1N NaOH.

The significance of this series of experiments may be sum-
marized as follows: (a) a toxic organophosphate insecticide,
parathion, was successfully biodegraded to simpler phosphoric
acids and phenols, (b) the microbial culture produced was able
to degrade six additional organophosphate pesticides, and (c)
the enzyme which was capable of hydrolyzing these biocides was
isolated and found to be stable outside the parent cell.

Dr. Münnecke is currently working with Bayer Farbenfabriken
of Leverkusen, West Germany to determine the feasibility of
using immobilized or free enzymes for the detoxification of
industrial pesticide production wastes. Preliminary results
show that free enzymes can be used to detoxify parathion in
formulations and production wastewaters, as well as in pesticide
containers. Current research is in progress to scale up to
40,000 liters of batch fermentations of mixed bacterial cultures.
Towards the end of this summer Münnecke hopes to begin pilot
studies for detoxification of 1,000 liters per hour of pesticide production wastewater.

In closing this address we wish to note that the MRI team
intends to visit several selected sites to obtain first-hand information on the state of the art of pesticide disposal research.

Literature Cited

1. Carnes, R. A., and D. A. Oberacker. Pesticide Incineration.
   (1976) U.S. Environmental Protection Agency, Municipal
   Environmental Research Laboratory.
2. Ferguson, T. L., F. J. Bergman, G. R. Cooper, R. T. Li, and
   F. I. Honea. Determination of Incinerator Operating Conditions Necessary for Safe Disposal of Pesticides. (1975)
   EPA-600/2-75-041.
3. Carnes, R. A. Thermal Degradation of Kepone®. (1977a) U.S.
   Environmental Protection Agency, Municipal Environmental
   Research Laboratory.
4. Duvall, D. S., and W. A. Rubey. Laboratory Evaluation of
   High Temperature Destruction of Kepone® and Related Pesticides, University of Dayton Research Institute. (1976)
   Technical Report UDRI-TR-76-21.
5. Carnes, R. A. EPA/MERL, Cincinnati. (1977b) Personal communication to R. R. Wilkinson.
6. Wastler, T. A., C. K. Offutt, C. K. Fitzsimmons, and P. E.
   Des Rosiers. Disposal of Organochlorine Wastes by Incineration of Sea. (1975) NTIS PB-253,979.
7. Environmental Sciences and Technology. (1977) 11(3):
   p. 236-237.

8. The Kansas City Times. (September 8, 1977) p. 13A.
9. Chemical and Engineering News. (September 12, 1977) p. 20.
10. Pesticide and Toxic Material News. (August 10, 1977) p. 33.
11. Astro Metallurgical Corporation. Wooster, Ohio. Summary of
    Waste Examples Reacted by Wet Oxidation Through 1976.
    (1977a) Form No. WT-77-3.
12. Astro Metallurgical Corporation. Astrol™ Wet Oxidation
    Waste Treatment Systems. (1977b) Form No. WT-77-1.
13. Adams, J. T., N. J. Cunningham, J. C. Harris, P. L. Levins,
    J. L. Stauffer, and K. E. Thrun. Destroying Chemical
    Wastes in Commercial-Scale Incinerators. (1976) NTIS PB-
    267. p. 987.
14. Environmental Sciences and Technology. (1974) $\underline{8}$(1): p. 18-19.
15. Krekeler, H., H. Meidert, W. Riemenschneider, and L. H.
    Hornig. U.S. Patent No. 3,651,157 issued March 21, 1972,
    and U.S. Patent No. 3,676,508 issued July 11, 1972.
16. Shiver, J. K. Converting Chlorohydrocarbon Wastes by Chlo-
    rolysis. (1976) NTIS PB-259. p. 935.
17. Des Rosiers, P. Industrial Pollution Control Division.
    (1977) Office of Research and Development, Environmental
    Protection Agency, Washington, D.C., Personal communication
    to R. R. Wilkinson. September.
18. Krekeler, H., H. Schmitz, and D. Rebhan. The High-Pressure
    Chlorolysis of Hydrocarbons to Carbon Tetrachloride--A
    New Process for the Utilization of Chlorinated Hydrocarbon
    Wastes. (1975) National Conference on the Management and
    Disposal of Residues for the Treatment of Industrial Waste-
    waters. Washington, D.C. February 3-5, 1975. Informa-
    tion Transfer, Inc., Rockville, Maryland.
19. Mauk, C. E., H. W. Prengle, Jr., and J. E. Payne. Oxidation
    of Pesticides by Ozone and Ultraviolet Light. (1976)
    NTIS AD-A028 306.
20. Münnecke, D. M. Properties of an Immobilized Pesticide-
    Hydrolyzing Enzyme. (1977) App. and Environ. Microbio.
    (1977) $\underline{33}$(3): p. 503-507.
21. Münnecke, D. M., and D. P. H. Hsieh. Development of Micro-
    bial Systems for the Disposal of Concentrated Pesticide
    Suspension. (1975) Meded. Fac. Landbuwwet. Rijksuniv.
    Gent. (1975) $\underline{40}$ (2, Pt. 2): p. 1,237-1,247. Chem. Abstr.
    (1976) $\underline{84}$, 131127d.
22. Hsieh, D. P. H., T. E. Archer, D. M. Münnecke, and F. E.
    McGowan. Decontamination of Noncombustible Agricultural
    Pesticide Containers by Removal of Emulsifiable Parathion.
    (1972) Environ. Sci. Tech. (1972) $\underline{6}$(9): p. 826-829.

Thermal Degradation of Selected Fungicides and Insecticides

MAURICE V. KENNEDY

Department of Biochemistry, Mississippi State University, Mississippi State, MS 39762

MILES E. HOLLOMAN

Propulsion Directorate, U.S. Army Missile Command, Redstone Arsenal, AL 35809

FAY Y. HUTTO

Mississippi State Chemical Laboratory, Mississippi State, MS 39762

One major problem facing agricultural leaders of today is the disposal of large quantities of waste pesticides without contamination of the environment. The wide variety of chemicals used as pesticides complicates the disposal problem by making it difficult to develop a single method of disposal which can be universally employed.

In the past settling ponds, ground burial, deep-well injection, and incineration have been the principal methods for disposal of chemical wastes (1). The first three procedures may not be suitable for disposal of large amounts of pesticides because they do not guarantee that the pesticides will remain at the disposal site. Pesticides may be transported over and through soil by either runoff or ground water (2). Thus, pesticide disposal by any of these methods might not only prevent future use of the disposal site for agricultural purposes but might also trigger widespread environmental pollution by these chemicals.

Incineration, however, has shown promise of being an efficient means of pesticide disposal (3). Since the aim of incineration is complete destruction of the pesticide molecule, a number of factors concerning the thermal degradation of pesticides must be determined in order for this process to be fully evaluated as a possible method of pesticide disposal. The degradation temperature for each compound considered as a possible candidate for incineration must be known. Moreover, combustion of pesticides may produce a number of toxic gases (4,5). Identities of all the potential pollutant gases produced by each pesticide must, therefore, be known in order to facilitate development of a scrubber system capable of minimizing air pollution. A comprehensive investigation of pesticide combustion products must also include products of incomplete combustion which may be formed under non-optimum combustion conditions, i.e., during an incinerator malfunction. The purpose of the present study was to provide preliminary information concerning the degradation of two fungicides and four insecticides and to identify the pollutant identify the pollutant gases produced under optimum and non-optimum conditions of pesticide incineration.

Experimental Section

Fungicides and Insecticides. The pesticides used in this investigation were the two fungicides and four insecticides studied under USDA Cooperative Agreement 12-14-7001-108. Analytical standards and commercial formulations were supplied by the respective manufacturers of the formulations. The chemical names of pesticides and the formulations used in this investigation are as follows:

Captan, N-(trichloromethylthio)-4 cyclohexene-1, 2-dicarboximide; Orthocide^R-50 wettable powder containing 50% active ingredient.

Maneb, manganeous ethylenebisdithio carbamate; Manzate^R wettable powder containing 80% active ingredient.

Methyl Parathion, O, O- dimethyl-O-p-nitrophenyl phosphorothioate; liquid Methyl Parathion 4-E containing 44% active ingredient.

Mirex, dodecachlorooctahydro-1,3,4-metheno-1H-cyclobutal [cd]pentalene; Mirex 4 containing 0.3% active ingredient (oil suspension on corn cob granules).

Temik, 2-methyl-2-(methylthio) propionaldehyde-O-(methylcarbamoyl) oxime; Temik^R-10G containing 10% active ingredient (10% temik^R impregnated on corn cob granules).

Toxaphene, a mixture of chlorinated camphenes of uncertain identity (combined chlorine content = 67-69%); liquid formulation containing 90% technical toxaphene and 10% xylene.

Fungicide and Insecticide Analysis. The concentration of active ingredient in each pesticide formulation was established by ten determinations. The mean values obtained are given in Table I. Gas-liquid chromatographic procedures were used for captan, methyl parathion, mirex, and toxaphene. Maneb was analyzed by the carbon disulfide evolution method (6) and temik by an infrared spectrophotometric method (7).

The captan, methyl parathion, and toxaphene formulations did not require cleanup. Captan was dissolved in acetone and methyl parathion and toxaphene in hexane. Aliquots of these solutions were diluted with hexane to the appropriate concentration for analysis.

The mirex formulation required the following cleanup procedure (8). Samples were dissolved in hexane and centrifuged to remove the insoluble materials. The supernatant liquid was transferred to a beaker containing deactivated florisil and mixed with the florisil. The dried mixture was extracted five times with petroleum ether and the combined extracts were evaporated to dryness. The residue was dissolved in hexane for analysis.

TABLE I

TEMPERATURES REQUIRED FOR PESTICIDE DEGRADATION IN OPEN AND CLOSED SYSTEMS

Pesticide	Melting Point (°C)	Type of Formulation[1]	Observed Active Ingredient (%)	Temperature of A. I. Elimination Open Crucible	Weight Loss (%)	Weight Loss at 1000°C (%)	Initial Degradation Temperature Sealed Ampule (°C)
Captan	172-173	WP	46.5	200	29.2	58.2	275
Maneb	Decomposes before melting	WP	80.0	200	37.0	72.2	200
Methyl Parathion	37-38	L	44.2	200	64.7	97.5	200
Mirex	Decomposes at 485	CC	0.3	300	47.9	99.3	525
Temik	98-100	CC	10.8	200	15.8	99.3	175
Toxaphene	65-90	L	90.2	400	94.2	99.9	250

[1] WP = Wettable powder, L = liquid, CC = corn cob support.

A Barber-Colman 5000 series gas chromatograph equipped with a tritium electron capture detector was employed for these analyses. The glass column, 6 ft. x 4 mm i.d., was packed with 1.5% OV-17, 1.95% QF-1 on 100/120 mesh Chromosorb W (9). Injector, column, and detector temperatures were 210°C, 200°C, and 210°C, respectively. The carrier gas was nitrogen at a flow rate of 100 ml/min.

Quantitation of the captan, methyl parathion, and mirex chromatograms was accomplished by the peak height method. The toxaphene chromatograms were quantitated by determining the total area under the toxaphene peaks using a Westronics Model 222 disc integrator. This method was determined to be 99.5% reproducible.

Muffle Furnace Treatments. The temperatures at which the active ingredient was completely eliminated from each formulation was determined in a muffle furnace in the following manner. Samples of the pesticides were weighed in Coors No. 0 porcelain crucibles and heated at 100°C increments from 100°C to 1000°C. Each determination was conducted in triplicate in the temperature range of 100°C to 500°C and in duplicate at the higher temperatures. The optimum time of heating for each pesticide was established by varying the time of heating at 100°C, 500°C, and 800°C. A heating time of 45 min was found to be sufficient to reach a point of no further reaction. The cooled samples were then analyzed for weight loss and content of active ingredient by the methods described previously. The criterion used for elimination of the active ingredient was no detectable amount of pesticide at the µg/ml level of residue concentration for the pesticides analyzed by gas chromatography and the mg/ml level for thos analyzed by wet methods. An untreated sample of the commercial formulation was analyzed as a quality control sample along with each group of heated samples.

Sealed Ampoule Determinations. The temperatures at which degradation of the analytical grade pesticides initiated was determined as follows. Samples were sealed in 10 ml ampoules and heated in a muffle furnace in increments of 25°C beginning at their melting points and continuing to some temperature at which degradation was confirmed. Sample sizes were approximately 20 mg and heating time was 15 min at each temperature. The criteria used to establish the temperature at which thermal degradation was initiated were the temperature at which the infrared spectrum deviated from that of the untreated pesticide due to the disappearance of one or more major absorptions and/or a change in physical appearance of the pesticide. All infrared spectra were obtained using 13 mm KBr pellets or CS_2 or CCl_4 solutions. The instrument was a Perkin-Elmer 337 grating spectrophotometer. Spectra of the untreated pesticides were compared to those in the Sadtler Index when possible (10).

Pollutant Gas Analysis. Two investigations were conducted to determine the volatile products of presticide combustion. The first study was the experimental determination of the gaseous products formed during heating in the temperature range of 400 - 525°C. Analytical grade pesticides (50-100 mg) were sealed in 10 ml ampoules and heated in a muffle furnace for 15 minutes. Identification of the gaseous products was accomplished by a combination of mass spectrometry and gas chromatography. The mass spectrometer was a Varian Anaspect EM-600 equipped with an EM 6270 gas sampling adapter. Gaseous samples were introduced with the adapter at an inlet temperature of 180°C. Spectra were obtained at ionizing voltages of 70 eV and approximately 25 eV and were interpreted by using a computer program. The program listed all possible combinations of the elements contained in a pesticide which would give each of the masses present in the spectrum of its gaseous products. The most probable gas (or gases) were selected for possible confirmation by gas chromatography using a Barber-Colman 5000 series chromatograph equipped with a thermal conductivity detector. All columns were 6 ft. by 4 mm i.d. glass columns. The following packings and conditions were used: (1) 80/100 mesh Deactigel; injector, column, and detector temperatures of 120°C, 120°C, and 125°C, respectively; carrier gas-helium at a flow rate of 50 ml/min (11); (2) 10% Arochlor 1232 on 40/60 mesh Chromosorb T; injector, column, and detector temperatures of 30°C, 30°C, and 100°C, respectively; carrier gas-helium at a flow rate of 15 ml/min (12).

The second study was the theoretical prediction of the combustion products which would results from incineration of the pesticides under conditions of complete combustion. Complete combustion was determined by the addition of successive amounts of air until a pesticide to air ratio was obtained at which a small excess of diatomic oxygen was present. Temperatures studied were 1727°C and 27°C. The NASA/LEWIS Chemical Equilibrum Composition Computer Program (13) was used to predict the products which would be thermodynamically stable under these conditions. This program, which contained the thermochemical properties of most of the combustion products to be expected from incineration of typical halogenated hydrocarbons, was amended to include the thermochemical properties of other compounds indicated to be present by the experimental data. The thermodynamic data were obtained from the literature (14-17).

Muffle Furnace Results. The temperatures at which the active ingredient was eliminated from each formulation and the accompanying weight losses at these temperatures are given in Table I. There are several possible pathways of pesticide loss during these treatments. Three of the possibilities are decomposition without volatilization, decomposition followed by volatilization of the products, and volatilization without decomposition. The weight losses indicate that in each instance

considerable quantities of gases were evolved at these temperatures. The residues remaining after heating captan, methyl
parathion and maneb at 1000°C were felt to be the result of the
presence of inorganic salts in the carrier or to formation of
such salts during heating. The low temperature at which mirex
could no longer be detected (Table I) led to the suspicion that
volatilization prior to degradation might be occurring in some
instances. This insecticide has previously been reported to be
thermally stable with pyrolysis occurring only about 500°C
(18,19).

Sealed Ampoule Results. Since there was no way to prevent
the escape of a volatile product from the crucibles, the minimum
temperatures at which degradation of the pesticides was initiated
was determined in sealed ampoules in order to prevent the
possibility of volatilization prior to degradation. Table I
also contains the results of this study. Comparison of the
open crucible and sealed ampoule results indicated the initial
degradation temperatures of maneb, methyl parathion, and temik
were similar to the temperatures at which the compounds were
eliminated from the residues in the crucibles. No vaporization
of maneb was observed in the ampoule at temperatures below the
initial degradation point. However, methyl parathion and temik
were similar to the temperatures at which the compounds were
eliminated from the residues in the crucibles. No vaporization
of maneb was observed in the ampoule at temperatures below the
initial degradation point. However, methyl parathion and temik
vaporized at 125°C and 150°C respectively. Initial degradation
temperatures of captan and mirex were considerably higher than
the temperatures at which these compounds disappeared from the
crucibles (Table I). These results support the theory that
these two compounds were volatilized from the crucible prior to
being degraded. Toxaphene appeared to be degraded in the
ampoule at a temperature considerably lower than the temperature
at which it was no longer detected in the crucible. However,
chromatograms of toxaphene heated to 300°C in the open crucible
showed an altering of composition as compared to the untreated
pesticide, and no toxaphene was detected in the residue produced
at 400°C. Volatilization of toxaphene in the ampoule was noted
at temperatures above 125°C.
        Results of these two studies seem to indicate that the
initial degradation temperatures determined in the sealed
ampoules are more accurate than those determined in the crucibles
because it was impossible for the pesticide to escape.

Pollutant Gas Analysis. The conditions used in the laboratory study were intended to simulate an incinerator malfunction
during which incomplete combustion would occur as the result of
the low temperature (400 - 525°C) and an insufficient oxygen

supply. The heating temperatures for all pesticides except mirex, were considerably higher than the minimum degradation temperatures determined in the sealed ampules.

Discussion of the gaseous combustion products is limited to pollutant gases. However, a number of other gases were present in all of the mixtures. For instance, the mass spectra indicated the presence of atmospheric nitrogen, oxygen and argon as well as the water vapor and carbon dioxide formed as a result of combustion. The presence of oxygen may have resulted from a leak in the gas sampling system. No special attempts were made to confirm any of these gases since they are not environmental hazards. The presence of CO was also not confirmed since it is a known product of incomplete combustion.

Incineration of maneb at 400°C produced a carbonaceous material. The mass spectrum consisted of 10 peaks, assignments of which are given in Table II. From this table it is obvious that the pollutant gases CH_4, NH_3, CO, and N_2O cannot be positively identified from the mass spectra because their masses are identical to the masses of other species (O, OH, N_2, and CO_2, respectively) which were present in most of the spectra. Pollutants tentatively identified from the spectrum of the maneb gaseous product mixture were N_2O, COS, and CS_2. The sulfur-containing gases, CO_2 and 20 were confirmed on the Deactigel column.

The residue remaining after heating methyl parathion at 400°C was also carbonaceous. The mass spectrum of the gaseous products was quite complex, containing 29 peaks. Assignments for these peaks are presented in Table II. Pollutants tentatively identified were HCN, NO_2, COS, SO_2, and CS_2. The presence of CO_2, COS, and CS_2 was confirmed on the Deactigel column and a peak with a retention identical to H_2S was also present in the chromatogram. Sulfur dioxide, however, was not confirmed and the peak at a mass of 64 was believed to have resulted from further fragmentation of the PSO_2^+ fragment (mass = 95).

Incineration of temik at 400°C produced a carbonaceous residue. The mass spectrum of the gaseous products contained 20 peaks. Assignments of these peaks are also listed in Table II. Pollutants tentatively identified from the spectrum were HCN and COS. The chromatogram resulting from passage of the gas mixture through the Deactigel column confirmed the presence of CO_2 and also contained two peaks with retention times identical to those of H_2S and CS_2. The concentration of COS in the gas mixture was evidently below the limit of detection of the chromatographic system.

The residue remaining after heating captan at 400°C was also carbonaceous. The mass spectrum of the gaseous products contained 14 peaks, assignments of which are given in Table III. Pollutant gases tentatively identified were HCL, COS, SO_2, CS_2, and $CHCl_3$. Confirmation of the sulfur-containing gases and CO_2 was accomplished with the Deactigel column. The chromatogram

TABLE II

MASS SPECTRAL DATA FOR SULFUR-CONTAINING PESTICIDES HEATED AT $400^{\circ}C$

AMU	Maneb		Methyl Parathion		Temik	
	Assignment	Confirmed by GC	Assignment	Confirmed by GC	Assignment	Confirmed by GC
14	N^+		N^+		N^+	
15	$--^*$		NH^+, CH_3^+		NH^+, CH_3^+	
16	--		O^+, NH_2^+, CH_4^+		O^+, NH_2^+, CH_4^+	
17	OH^+, NH_3^+		OH^+, NH_3^+		OH^+, NH_3^+	
18	H_2O^+		H_2O^+		H_2O^+	
27	--		HCN^+		HCN^+	
28	N_2^+, CO^+		N_2^+, CO^+		N_2^+, CO^+	
29	--		$14,15_{N_2}^+$		$14,15_{N_2}^+$	
32	O_2^+		O_2^+		O_2^+	
35	--		Unidentified		--	
40	Ar^+		Ar^+		Ar^+	
41	--		--		$C_3H_5^+$, $C_2H_3N^+$	
42	--		--		$C_3H_6^+$	
43	--		--		$C_3H_7^+$	
44	CO_2^+	Yes	CO_2^+	Yes	CO_2^+	Yes
	N_2O^+	Yes	N_2O^+		N_2O^+	
45	--		CH_2P^+, CO_2H^+		CO_2H^+	
46	--		CH_3P^+, NO_2^+		--	
47	--		CH_4P^+, PO^+		--	
48	--		CH_5P^+, SO^+		--	
49	--		Unidentified		--	

TABLE II (Cont'd)

AMU	Maneb		Methyl Parathion		Temik	
	Assignment	Confirmed by GC	Assignment	Confirmed by GC	Assignment	Confirmed by GC
57	--		$C_2H_2P^+$		--	
58	--		$C_2H_3P^+$		CO_2N^+, $C_2H_2S^+$	
59	--		$C_2H_4P^+$		--	
60	COS^+	Yes	COS^+	Yes	COS^+	
61	--		$C_2H_6P^+$, CH_2PO^+		--	
62	--		$C_2H_7P^+$, CH_3PO^+		--	
63	---		PO_2^+, PS^+		----	
64	--		SO_2^+		--	
76	CS_2^+	Yes	CS_2^+	Yes	--	
79	--		PO_3^+, PSO^+		$CH_3SO_2^+$, $CH_3S_2^+$	
94	--		--		$C_2H_6SO_2^+$, $C_2H_6S_2^+$	
95	--		PSO_2^+		--	

* -- Means that no peak occurred at the specified mass number.

TABLE III

MASS SPECTRAL DATA FOR CAPTAN AND TOXAPHENE HEATED AT $400^{\circ}C$ AND MIREX HEATED AT $525^{\circ}C$

AMU	Captan Assignment	Captan Confirmed by GC	Mirex Assignment	Mirex Confirmed by GC	Toxaphene Assignment	Toxaphene Confirmed by GC
14	$--^{*}$		N^{+}, CH_2^{+}		N^{+}, CH_2^{+}	
16	--		O^{+}, CH_4^{+}		O^{+}, CH_4^{+}	
17	--		OH^{+}		OH^{+}	
18	H_2O^{+}		H_2O^{+}		H_2O^{+}	
27	--		--		$C_2H_3^{+}$	
28	N_2^{+}, CO^{+}		N_2^{+}, CO^{+}		N_2^{+}, CO^{+}	
32	O_2^{+}		O_2^{+}		O_2^{+}	
35	--		Cl^{+}		Cl^{+}	
36	HCl^{+}		HCl^{+}	Yes	HCl^{+}	
37	--		$^{37}Cl^{+}$		$^{37}Cl^{+}$	
38	$H^{37}Cl^{+}$		$H^{37}Cl^{+}$	Yes	$H^{37}Cl^{+}$	
40	Ar^{+}		Ar^{+}		Ar^{+}	
44	CO_2^{+}	Yes	CO_2^{+}	Yes	CO_2^{+}	Yes
45	--		--		CO_2H^{+}	
47	--		CCl^{+}		--	
48	$CHCl^{+}$		--		--	
49	--		$C^{37}Cl^{+}$		--	
60	COS^{+}	Yes	--		--	
61	--		--		$C_2H_2Cl^{+}$	
62	--		--		$C_2H_3Cl^{+}$	
63	--		$COCl^{+}$		$COCl^{+}, C_2H_4Cl^{+}, C_2H_2^{37}Cl^{+}$	

TABLE III (Cont'd)

AMU	Captan		Mirex		Toxaphene	
	Assignment	Confirmed by GC	Assignment	Confirmed by GC	Assignment	Confirmed by GC
64	SO_2^+	Yes	--		--	
65	--		$CO^{37}Cl^+$		--	
70	--		Cl_2^+	Yes	Cl_2^+	
72	--		$^{35}Cl^{37}Cl^+$	Yes	$^{35}Cl^{37}Cl^+$	
76	CS_2^+	Yes	--		--	
78	$CS^{34}S^+$	Yes	--		--	
82	--		CCl_2^+		--	
83	$CHCl_2^+$		--		--	
84	--		$CCl^{37}Cl^+$		--	
85	$CHCl^{37}Cl^+$		--		--	
86	--		$C^{37}Cl_2^+$		--	
96	--		--		$C_2H_2Cl_2^+$	
98	--		$COCl_2^+$		$COCl_2^+$, $C_2H_4Cl_2^+$,	
100	--		$COCl^{37}Cl^+$		-- $C_2H_2Cl^{37}Cl^+$	
117	--		CCl_3^+		CCl_3^+	
119	--		$CCl_2^{37}Cl^+$		$CCl_2^{37}Cl^+$	
121	--		$CCl^{37}Cl_2^+$		--	
123	--		$C^{37}Cl_3^+$		--	
152	--		CCl_4^+	Yes	--	
154	--		$CCl_3^{37}Cl^+$	Yes	--	
156	--		$CCl_2^{37}Cl_2^+$	Yes	--	

* -- means that no peak occurred at the specified mass number.

also contained a peak with a retention time identical to that of H_2S.

Mirex was more resistant to thermal degradation than any of the other pesticides. Even after heating at 525°C the residue was not carbonaceous but consisted of long, off-white crystals and liquid droplets. The mass spectrum of the gaseous products consisted of 30 fragments, assignments of which are presented in Table III. The toxic gases tentatively identified were identical to those resulting from incineration of mirex at 550°C (20). Confirmation of HCl, Cl_2, and CCl_4 was accomplished with the Arochlor 1232 column and carbon dioxide was confirmed on the Deactigel column.

The residue remaining after heating toxaphene at 400°C consisted of a carbonaceous solid and a black liquid. The mass spectrum of the gaseous products contained of 23 fragments, assignments of which are given in Table III. The primary pollutant was HCl. Other possibilities tentatively identified from the spectrum were C_2H_3Cl, C_2H_5Cl, Cl_2, $C_2H_2Cl_2$, $COCl_2$, $C_2H_4Cl_2$, and CCl_4. Vinyl chloride was confirmed on the Deactigel column but no C_2H_4Cl was detected. The presence of CCl_4 was confirmed on the Arochlor 1232 column.

The complete combustion products predicted by the thermodynamic calculations are given in Tables IV and V. The number of moles of air required for complete combustion of one mole of pesticide was 50 for mirex, 55 for captan, temik, and toxaphene, and 60 for maneb and methyl parathion. The higher temperature represents the operating range of commercial incinerators while the lower temperature simulates the cooled exhaust. The equilibrium product distributions are presented as the mole fraction of each product formed from the theoretical incineration of each pesticide in the presence of the specified moles of air.

The major products predicted under these conditions were rather simple except for those resulting from the presence of manganese in maneb and phosphorus in methyl parathion. The carbon component was oxidized primarily to CO_2 with small quantities of CO also being formed. Pesticide nitrogen was converted mainly to N_2 and small amounts of NO. Most of the hydrogen formed H_2O or HCl. Sulfur was oxidized primarily to SO_2 and SO_3 except for maneb. Chlorine was converted mainly to HCl or Cl_2. Maneb was the only pesticide which yielded solid products at high temperatures. At 1727°C the manganese was oxidized to MnO (Table IV). This compound then reacted with the sulfur oxides as the gases were cooled to form $MnSO_4$. The phosphorus in methyl parathion was converted mainly to PO_2 and P_4O_6 at 1727°C and P_4O_{10} at 27°C (Table IV).

The results of this study were somewhat simplified by the use of a thermodynamic model to predict the products of incineration. Three of the systems affected by the neglect of kinetics were the CO, NO, and SO_2-SO_3 systems.

In recent years the kinetics of CO and NO formation and destruction have been widely investigated (21,22). Results of these investigations indicate that actual CO concentrations in automobile exhaust are similar to the equilibrium values at the combustion temperatures rather than the equilibrium values at the exhaust temperatures. Nitric oxide formation has been found to occur by two routes. The first path is oxidation of atmospheric nitrogen at temperatures above 1760°C by the following reactions.

$$N_2 + O\cdot \longrightarrow NO + N\cdot$$

$$N\cdot + O_2 \longrightarrow NO + O\cdot$$

$$N + OH \longrightarrow NO + H\cdot$$

The other route is the oxidation of pesticide nitrogen. Kinetics of this reaction are of the same order as the combustion process. Kinetics of CO and NO destruction, however, are limited during expansion. As a result, considerable quantities of these gases will probably be present in incinerator exhaust.

Although the calculations indicated that the sulfur will be converted to SO_2 and SO_3 (Tables IV and V), studies of exhaust gases from sulfur-containing fuels have indicated that only 1-3% of the sulfur will be oxidized to SO_3 (23). This finding indicates that considerable SO_2 will probably be present in incinerator exhaust during combustion of sulfur-containing pesticides even though none was predicted by the thermodynamic model. Moreover, the SO_3 formed will react with H_2O to yield H_2SO_4 (23).

Conclusions

Heating of fungicides and insecticides under both optimum and non-optimum conditions of combustion produced a number of potential air pollutants. On a practical basis all of these gases must be scrubbed from the incinerator effluent prior to its discharge into the atmosphere. Therefore, a scrubber system capable of absorbing the pollutant gases must be developed before incineration can be utilized as a method of disposal for these pesticides.

Abstract

Degradation of six selected fingicides and insecticides was investigated in both open and closed systems. There was evidence that vaporization prior to degradtion could occur in open crucibles. Initial degradation temperatures determined in sealed ampoules were 275°C for captan, 200°C for maneb and methyl parathion, 525°C for mirex, 175°C for temik, and 250°C

TABLE IV

COMBUSTION PRODUCTS* OF SULFUR-CONTAINING PESTICIDES IN AIR

Combustion and Exhaust Temperatures (°C)

Product	Maneb		Methyl Parathion		Temik	
	1727	27	1727	27	1727	27
Ar	8.85×10^{-3}	9.30×10^{-3}	8.52×10^{-3}	8.72×10^{-3}	8.45×10^{-3}	8.53×10^{-3}
CO	4.16×10^{-4}	0.00	8.15×10^{-4}	0.00	1.18×10^{-3}	0.00
CO_2	6.33×10^{-2}	6.70×10^{-2}	1.13×10^{-1}	1.25×10^{-1}	1.15×10^{-1}	1.17×10^{-1}
H	1.33×10^{-5}	0.00	1.71×10^{-5}	0.00	2.61×10^{-5}	0.00
HNO	1.16×10^{-8}	0.00	1.42×10^{-8}	0.00	1.42×10^{-8}	0.00
NO_2	2.81×10^{-7}	9.51×10^{-29}	3.48×10^{-7}	2.16×10^{-28}	2.26×10^{-7}	8.79×10^{-29}
H_2	6.83×10^{-5}	0.00	1.12×10^{-4}	0.00	2.60×10^{-4}	0.00
$H_2O(L)$	0.00	1.66×10^{-2}	0.00	4.53×10^{-2}	0.00	8.51×10^{-2}
H_2O	4.71×10^{-2}	3.34×10^{-2}	7.56×10^{-2}	3.28×10^{-2}	1.15×10^{-1}	3.16×10^{-2}
H_2O_2	1.77×10^{-8}	1.17×10^{-24}	2.79×10^{-8}	2.00×10^{-24}	2.77×10^{-8}	1.09×10^{-24}
H_2S	1.51×10^{-10}	0.00	0.00	0.00	3.61×10^{-10}	0.00
N	7.75×10^{-10}	0.00	7.63×10^{-10}	0.00	7.65×10^{-10}	0.00
NH	1.12×10^{-10}	0.00	1.40×10^{-10}	0.00	2.14×10^{-10}	0.00
NO	3.43×10^{-3}	7.34×10^{-17}	3.31×10^{-3}	1.22×10^{-16}	2.16×10^{-3}	6.74×10^{-17}
NO_2	2.40×10^{-6}	9.86×10^{-12}	2.26×10^{-6}	2.87×10^{-11}	9.63×10^{-7}	8.91×10^{-12}
N_2	7.57×10^{-1}	7.98×10^{-1}	7.21×10^{-1}	7.40×10^{-1}	7.25×10^{-1}	7.32×10^{-1}
N_2O	1.71×10^{-7}	5.47×10^{-20}	1.60×10^{-7}	8.85×10^{-21}	1.05×10^{-7}	4.94×10^{-20}
O	1.30×10^{-4}	0.00	1.29×10^{-4}	0.00	6.45×10^{-5}	0.00
OH	8.98×10^{-4}	5.89×10^{-28}	1.14×10^{-3}	7.65×10^{-28}	1.13×10^{-3}	5.53×10^{-28}
O_2	3.90×10^{-2}	9.50×10^{-3}	3.80×10^{-2}	2.84×10^{-2}	1.62×10^{-2}	8.71×10^{-3}

TABLE IV (Cont'd)

Product	Combustion and Exhaust Temperatures (°C)					
	Maneb		Methyl Parathion		Temik	
	1727	27	1727	27	1727	27
O_3	3.98×10^{-10}	3.53×10^{-32}	3.80×10^{-10}	1.84×10^{-31}	1.06×10^{-10}	3.18×10^{-32}
S	1.14×10^{-8}	0.00	2.85×10^{-9}	0.00	7.24×10^{-9}	0.00
SH	1.59×10^{-9}	0.00	5.06×10^{-10}	0.00	1.95×10^{-9}	0.00
SO	4.73×10^{-5}	0.00	1.16×10^{-5}	0.00	1.92×10^{-5}	0.00
SO_2	6.33×10^{-2}	2.44×10^{-13}	1.52×10^{-2}	4.37×10^{-14}	1.65×10^{-2}	8.27×10^{-14}
SO_3	7.13×10^{-5}	5.00×10^{-2}	1.68×10^{-5}	1.56×10^{-2}	1.19×10^{-5}	1.67×10^{-2}
SN	1.40×10^{-10}	0.00	0.00	0.00	0.00	0.00
$MnO(s)$	1.59×10^{-2}	0.00	0.00	0.00	0.00	0.00
$MnSO_4(s)$	0.00	1.67×10^{-2}	0.00	0.00	0.00	0.00
PN	0.00	0.00	1.93×10^{-8}	0.00	0.00	0.00
PO	0.00	0.00	9.38×10^{-6}	0.00	0.00	0.00
PO_2	0.00	0.00	1.41×10^{-2}	0.00	0.00	0.00
P_4O_6	0.00	0.00	3.01×10^{-4}	0.00	0.00	0.00
$P_4O_{10}(s)$	0.00	0.00	0.00	3.92×10^{-3}	0.00	0.00
P_4O_{10}	0.00	0.00	6.00×10^{-8}	2.71×10^{-8}	0.00	0.00

* mole fractions
L = liquid
S = solid.

TABLE V

COMBUSTION PRODUCTS* OF CHLORINATED PESTICIDES IN AIR

| | Combustion and Exhaust Temperatures (°C) | | | | | |
| | Captan | | Mirex | | Toxaphene | |
Product	1727	27	1727	27	1727	27
Ar	8.40×10^{-3}	8.60×10^{-3}	7.74×10^{-3}	8.30×10^{-3}	8.07×10^{-3}	8.32×10^{-3}
CO	1.40×10^{-3}	0.00	2.36×10^{-3}	0.00	1.56×10^{-3}	0.00
COCl	3.79×10^{-9}	0.00	1.55×10^{-7}	0.00	1.78×10^{-8}	0.00
COCl$_2$	0.00	0.00	5.69×10^{-9}	3.08×10^{-34}	1.14×10^{-10}	2.73×10^{-29}
CO$_2$	1.47×10^{-1}	1.52×10^{-1}	1.64×10^{-1}	1.79×10^{-1}	1.56×10^{-1}	1.63×10^{-1}
Cl	5.58×10^{-3}	8.40×10^{-20}	1.34×10^{-1}	1.76×10^{-19}	2.35×10^{-2}	1.19×10^{-19}
ClO	1.14×10^{-5}	3.43×10^{-20}	1.82×10^{-4}	3.24×10^{-19}	4.59×10^{-5}	1.05×10^{-24}
ClO$_2$	2.08×10^{-10}	3.15×10^{-26}	2.19×10^{-5}	1.34×10^{-24}	7.98×10^{-10}	2.12×10^{-35}
Cl$_2$	5.60×10^{-5}	2.52×10^{-2}	3.25×10^{-2}	1.07×10^{-1}	9.92×10^{-4}	4.95×10^{-2}
Cl$_2$O	0.00	0.00	1.76×10^{-8}	4.87×10^{-21}	7.76×10^{-10}	1.09×10^{-26}
H	1.55×10^{-5}	0.00	0.00	0.00	8.50×10^{-6}	0.00
HCl	4.36×10^{-2}	1.02×10^{-4}	0.00	0.00	1.01×10^{-1}	3.11×10^{-2}
HO	8.96×10^{-9}	0.00	0.00	0.00	4.58×10^{-9}	0.00
HO$_2$	1.56×10^{-7}	8.90×10^{-30}	0.00	0.00	7.82×10^{-8}	9.21×10^{-37}
H$_2$	9.14×10^{-5}	0.00	0.00	0.00	2.76×10^{-5}	1.25×10^{-35}
H$_2$O(L)	0.00	3.38×10^{-2}	0.00	0.00	0.00	1.55×10^{-2}
H$_2$O	4.34×10^{-2}	3.34×10^{-2}	0.00	0.00	1.25×10^{-2}	3.40×10^{-2}
H$_2$O$_2$	1.13×10^{-8}	2.40×10^{-25}	0.00	0.00	3.11×10^{-9}	5.33×10^{-30}
H$_2$S	1.09×10^{-10}	0.00	0.00	0.00	0.00	0.00

TABLE V (Cont'd)

Product	Captan (°C)		Mirex (°C)		Toxaphene (°C)	
	1727	27	1727	27	1727	27
N	7.58×10^{-10}	0.00	7.23×10^{-10}	0.00	7.39×10^{-10}	0.00
NH	1.26×10^{-10}	0.00	0.00	0.00	0.00	0.00
NO	2.31×10^{-3}	1.45×10^{-17}	1.46×10^{-3}	6.49×10^{-17}	2.15×10^{-3}	3.11×10^{-22}
NOCl	1.40×10^{-7}	8.25×10^{-15}	2.13×10^{-6}	7.50×10^{-14}	5.50×10^{-7}	2.47×10^{-19}
NO_2	1.12×10^{-6}	4.01×10^{-13}	4.65×10^{-7}	8.10×10^{-12}	9.92×10^{-7}	1.88×10^{-22}
N_2	7.12×10^{-1}	7.30×10^{-1}	6.49×10^{-1}	6.97×10^{-1}	6.76×10^{-1}	6.99×10^{-1}
N_2O	1.11×10^{-7}	1.03×10^{-20}	6.69×10^{-8}	4.44×10^{-20}	1.01×10^{-7}	2.15×10^{-25}
O	9.11×10^{-5}	0.00	6.02×10^{-5}	0.00	8.70×10^{-5}	0.00
OH	7.22×10^{-4}	2.67×10^{-28}	0.00	0.00	3.79×10^{-4}	0.00
O_2	1.88×10^{-2}	4.04×10^{-4}	8.23×10^{-3}	8.48×10^{-3}	1.72×10^{-2}	1.95×10^{-3}
O_3	1.32×10^{-10}	3.09×10^{-34}	0.00	0.00	1.16×10^{-10}	0.00
S	6.20×10^{-9}	0.00	0.00	0.00	0.00	0.00
SH	9.93×10^{-10}	0.00	0.00	0.00	0.00	0.00
SO	1.77×10^{-5}	0.00	0.00	0.00	0.00	0.00
SO_2	1.64×10^{-2}	3.99×10^{-13}	0.00	0.00	0.00	0.00
SO_3	1.27×10^{-5}	1.68×10^{-2}	0.00	0.00	0.00	0.00

* mole fractions
l. - liquid.

for toxaphene. Gaseous products produced by heating the pesticides in the temperature range of 400-525°C were identified by
mass spectrometry and gas chromatography. Toxic gases identified
included HCN, H_2S, HCl, NO_2, COS, SO_2, CS_2, Cl_2, $CHCl_3$, CCl_4,
$COCl_2$, and C_2H_3Cl. Products resulting from complete combustion
were predicted by a series of chemical equilibrum composition
calculations. These products included CO_2, CO, N_2, NO, H_2O, HCl,
Cl_2, SO_2, SO_3, $MnSO_4$, PO_2, P_4O_6, and P_4O_{10}.

Literature Cited

1.   Woodland, R. G., Hall, M. C., Russell, R. R., J. Air Pollu-
      tion Cont. Assoc. (1965) 15, 56.
2.   Stojanovic, B. J., Kennedy, M. V., Shuman, F. L., Jr., J.
      Environ. Quality (1972) 1, 54.
3.   Kennedy, M. V., Stojanovic, B. J., Shuman, F. L., Jr.,
      Residue Rev. (1969) 29, 89.
4.   Kennedy, M. V., Stojanovic, B. J., Shuman, F. L., Jr. Agr.
      Food Chem. (1972a) 20, 341.
5.   Kennedy, M. V., Stojanovic, B. J., Shuman, F. L., Jr., J.
      Environ. Quality (1972b) 1, 63.
6.   Zweig, G., Ed., "Analytical Methods for Pesticides, Plant
      Growth Regulators. and Food Additives," Vol. III, Academic
      Press, New York, 1964, pp. 71-74.
7.   McDermott, W. H., J. Ass. Off. Anal. Chem. (1973) 56, 1091.
8.   Jackson, E. R., Mississippi State Chemical Laboratory,
      Mississippi State, MS, private communication, 1974.
9.   Thompson, J. F., Ed., "Analysis of Pesticide Residues in
      Human and Environmental Samples," Primate and Pesticide
      Effects Laboratory, Environmental Protection Agency, Perrine,
      FL, 1972, Sections 3B and 4A.
10.   Sadtler Research Laboratories, Inc., "Sadtler Standard
      Spectra," Philadelphia, PA, 1968.
11.   Thornsberry, W. L., Jr., Anal. Chem. (1971) 43, 452.
12.   Bethea, R. M., Meador, M. C., J. Chromatogr. Sci. (1969) 7,
      655.
13.   Gordon, S., McBride, B. J., "Computer Program for Calcula-
      tion of Complex Chemical Equilibrium Compositions, Rocket
      Performance, Incident and Reflected Shocks, and Chapman-
      Jouguet Detonations," NASA SP-237, 1971.
14.   Barin, I., Knacke, O., "Thermochemical Properties of
      Inorganic Substances," Springer-Verlag, Berlin/Heidelburg,
      1973.
15.   Chase, M. W., Curnutt, J. L., Hu, A. T., Prophet, H.,
      Syverud, A. N., Walker, L. C., J. Phys. Chem. Data (1974)
      3, 311.
16.   National Bureau of Standards, JANAF Thermochemical Tables,
      Second Edition, National Standard Reference Data System -
      National Bureau of Standards 37, 1971.

17. Rossini, F. D., Wagman, D. D., Evans, W. H., Levine, S., Jaffe, I., "Selected Values of Chemical Thermodynamic Properties," Circular 500, National Bureau of Standards, February 1, 1952.

18. Eaton, P., Carlson, E., Lombardo, P., Yates, P., J. Org. Chem. (1960) 25, 1225.

19. McBee, E. T., Roberts, C. W., Idol, J. D., Jr., Earle, R. H., J. Amer. Chem. Soc. (1956) 78, 1511.

20. Holloman, M. E., Layton, B. R., Kennedy, M. V., Swanson, C. R., accepted for publication in J. Agr. Food Chem., June 12, 1975.

21. Newhall, H. K., Twelfth Symposium (International) on Combustion, The Combustion Institute, Pittsburgh, PA, 1969, p. 635.

22. Breen, B. P., Bell, A. W., DeVolo, N. B., Bagwell, F. A., Rosenthal, K., Thirteenth Symposium (International) on Combustion, the Combustion Institute, Pittsburgh, PA, 1971, p. 391.

23. Nettleton, M. A., Stirling, R., Twelfth Symposium (International) on Combustion, The Combustion Instutute, Pittsburgh, PA, 1969, p. 635.

MARCH 23, 1978

8

Developing Technology for Detoxification of Pesticides and Other Hazardous Materials

CHARLES J. ROGERS

U.S. Environmental Protection Agency, Cincinnati, OH 45268

ROBERT ALLEN

U.S. Environmental Protection Agency, Philadelphia, PA 19106

Promising technologies are continuously being developed to reduce the impact of toxic and hazardous materials (whether liquid, semi-liquid, or solid) on the environment. Although in the past excess materials have been disposed of by the quickest, easiest, and most economical means available, a recent increase in the supply of agricultural chemicals and, more importantly, an increase in concern for the environment places new emphasis on treatments needed prior to disposal.

Specialized techniques investigated by the U.S. Environmental Protection Agency (USEPA) for detoxification of toxic and hazardous materials include wet oxidation, chlorinolysis, sulfonation, catalysis, incineration, micro-wave plasma, encapsulation, and experimental disposal pits that prevent the loss of unwanted material while allowing biodegradation. The last, a promising technique for treatment of pesticides used by farmers and agricultural and commercial applicators, is discussed in this paper.

Pit Disposal of Excess Hazardous Materials. Ongoing work at Iowa State University includes development of a simple technique for the disposal of pesticides left unused in ground or aerial application operations. At present the safety and effectiveness of the various disposal systems in use by applicators have not been documented to the extent that USEPA can recommend this technique over others.

Since 1967, Iowa State University has developed and used a simple plastic-lined disposal pit at the Agronomy and Agricultural Engineering Research Station near Ames. In 1973, a more sophisticated concrete-lined pit was constructed at the Horticultural Research Station shown in Figure 1.

There had been no monitoring of either pit for effective degradation, possible loss by volatilization, or possible concentration of hazardous pesticides. To obtain adequate data on the disposal pits, a USEPA grant was awarded October 1975 to Iowa State University--specifically, to evaluate the

effectiveness of pits currently in use and to determine the
factors and parameters for improving the technique.
Some of the pesticides used at the Horticulture Station
and deposited in the specialized pit are shown in Table I.

TABLE I

CHEMICALS USED AT HORTICULTURE STATION

Small amounts of leftover diluted materials were deposited.

Insecticides

Carbaryl 50% (sevin)	Toxophene E.L. (6 lb/gal)
Chlordane 50%	Guthion 50% W.P.
Kelthane 35%	Lannate 90%
Pyrethrum 20%	Heptachlor 30.2% + Xylene 44%
Cythion 25% W.P.	

Herbicides

Dacthal	Amiben 23% W.P.
2,4-D	Tenoran 50% W.P.
Paraquat	Casoron

Fungicides

Benlate	Maneb
Bravo 6F 54%	Zineb
Benlate	Sulfur
Captan	

The chemical and microbiological studies, although incomplete, have revealed that many of the pesticides disposed in the
pits can still be detected. Tables II and III show pesticide
concentrations in ppm for the horticultural farm disposal pit as
sampled in March and June of 1977. Microbiological studies also
have shown that gram negative bacterial species thrive in the
pits and actively degrade selected pesticides.
    To determine the chemical alteration of pesticides in the
horticultural disposal pit, a minipit experiment is being conducted as part of the larger project by personnel from the
Departments of Agricultural Engineering, Agronomy, Bacteriology,
Botany and Plant Pathology, Energy and Mineral Resource Research Institute, and Entomology at Iowa State University.
    The slides for the oral presentation (174th meeting of the
American Chemical Society, Chicago, August 30, 1977) were taken
April 27, 1977, when pretreatment samples were taken and pesticides were added to the minipits.

TABLE II

Amount of Pesticides in PPM at the Horticultural Farm Disposal Pit - March 1977

Pesticide	Sample Type	PPM AT VARIOUS SAMPLING POINTS							
		#1	#2	#3	#4	#5	#6	#7	#8
Guthion	H_2O	2.8	1.5	2.1	8.1	4.0	2.9	3.8	2.1
	Soil	309	74	124	1784	3064	124	3767	13
Bravo	H_2O	0.14	0.46	0.03	0.52	0.26	0.20	0.22	0.23
	Soil	3296	4583	296	309	489	19	548	367
Dacthal	H_2O	0.24	0.30	0.23	0.35	0.21	0.26	0.28	0.31
	Soil	358	411	32	2923	3548	64	1718	53
Ramrod	H_2O	13.9	11.5	13.0	46.2	57.7	11.6	7.8	11.1
	Soil								
Hexachloro-benzene	H_2O	0.15	0.12	0.13	0.25	0.16	0.12	0.15	0.11
	Soil	19.6	63.7	0.50	202	123	3.5	74.8	5.9
Endosulfan I	H_2O				0.29				
	Soil	57.3	9.9	6.2	104	65.7	3.4	11.2	2.2
Endosulfan II	H_2O				0.15				
	Soil	33.0	5.1	4.0	66.7	29.6	1.7	4.7	1.7

TABLE III

Amount of Pesticides in PPM at the Horticultural Farm Disposal Pit - June 1977

Pesticide	Sample Type	PPM AT VARIOUS SAMPLING POINTS							
		#1	#2	#3	#4	#5	#6	#7	#8
Guthion	H_2O	205	20	118	916	191	78	92	28
	Soil	.06	.64	.28	.11	.09	.14	.44	1.39
Bravo	H_2O	118	200	38	593	67	43	30	485
	Soil	.85	.14	.45	6.35	.20	.19	.72	5.05
Dacthal	H_2O	452	4	29	13376	14	36	280	45
	Soil								
Ramrod	H_2O	21	29	96	155	32	159	151	90
	Soil				57	163	9.2		
Hexachloro-benzene	H_2O	0.11	0.08	0.07	50	0.17	0.26	0.11	0.25
	Soil	25.0	9.2	7.0	300	27.4	11.0	20.0	3.5
Endosulfan I	H_2O	0.51	0.25	0.11	0.57	0.04	0.05	0.03	0.14
	Soil	26.6	6.9	3.2	15.3	4.2	1.5	0.8	1.0
Endosulfan II	H_2O	0.20	0.07	0.03	0.33	0.02	0.02		0.03
	Soil	11.3	6.5	1.2	10.4	1.7			

Figure 1.   Concrete-lined disposal pit

Figure 2.   An overall view of the minipit area

Figure 3.   Closer view of shed and polyvinyl chlor-
ide compressed air manifold

*Figure 4.   Adding water to a garbage can contain-
ing soil (15 kg) to make a total volume of 60 L*

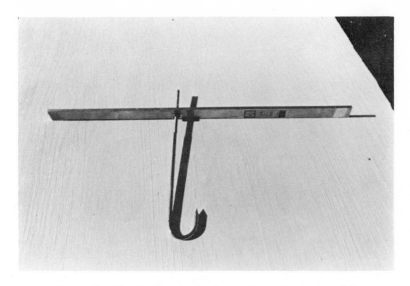

Figure 5.   Closeup of water level gage shown in previous slide

Figure 6.   Electric motor and propeller stirrer used to mix soil, water, and pesticide(s) in each garbage can

Figure 7.   Addition of a wettable powder formulation of carbaryl (see Table II) to Minipit 3E

Figure 8.   Continuation of mixing prior to obtaining a sample for analysis

Figure 9.   Obtaining samples for analysis: a 4-oz jar with a 2-hole rubber stopper (holes in a vertical position) is moved slowly from top to bottom twice in the process of taking a sample

Figure 10.   Addition of emulsifiable concentrate formulation of Alachlor to Minipit 5G

Figure 11.   Obtaining sample for bacteriological analysis immediately after sampling for chemical analysis

Figure 12.   Weather station within a few hundred feet of the minipit area. Weather information will be available for comparison of the analytical data.

The minipit experiment consists of fifty-six (56) thirty (30) gallon polyethylene garbage cans partially buried in the ground and arranged in seven 8-can rows (Figure 2). Four rows contain herbicides (alachlor, atrazine, 2,4-D, and trifluralin), with one herbicide per row in different amounts and concentrations. Two rows contain insecticides (carbaryl and parathion), one per row, again in different amounts and concentrations. The last row contains mixtures of all six pesticides. The eight garbage cans per row alternately contain 300 gram, 0.5% (w/w) and 15 gram, 0.025% (w/w) pesticide samples. The 0.5% (w/w) concentration represents a reasonable, practical application concentration. The 0.025% (w/w) concentration approximates the dilution one might obtain by rinsing the tank on equipment used to apply the pesticide.

Half of the cans contain 0.1% (w/v) peptone as a nutrient. The contents of half the cans (some with, some without nutrients) are aerated using a small compressor, a polyvinyl chloride manifold, and tygon tubing leading to each fritted glass aerator. The entire area is protected by a wire fence and warning signs. Garbage can lids are kept in place between sampling periods.

Analyses and evaluations for both the minipits and large pit will be completed by November 1978. It is expected that the results will show whether a low-cost, improved pit disposal system can be developed and recommended for wide-scale use in the disposal of unwanted pesticides.

Summary. The pesticide disposal pit (macro) located at Iowa State University's horticulture station has been in use for seven years. Water and soil samples were analyzed during the 1976-77 growing season for chemical, biological and microbial activity and content. The major finding, as substantiated by chemical and microbiological data, is that no build-up of pesticide residues in the pit occurs. Sampling and analyzing of the pit at various locations revealed that inhomogeneity of pesticide distribution existed. Consequently, minipit experiments were designed to determine trends in pesticide degradation, and the overall fate of pesticides disposed of in the pits.

It is expected that at the conclusion of 1978, sufficient data will be available for full-scale demonstration of this disposal technique.

MARCH 23, 1978

9

Pyrolysis and Disposal of Mirex Residues

BOBBY R. LAYTON and EARL G. ALLEY

Mississippi State Chemical Laboratory, Box CR, Mississippi State, MS 39762

At the request of the Mississippi Imported Fire Ant Authori-
ty, methods were investigated for the disposal of shipment drums
contaminated with mirex, 1,2,3,4,5,5,6,7,8,9,10,10 dodecachloro-
pentacyclo [5.3.0.0^{2,6}.0^{3,9}.0^{4,8}] decane (I). Extensive chemical
studies on mirex (1, 2, 3) showed that this compound is thermally
stable and resistant to most common oxidizing and reducing
systems. However, mirex has been shown to dechlorinate photochemically (4, 5, 6). Mirex has also been found to undergo reductive dechlorination in the presence of reduced hematin (7)
and when incubated under anaerobic conditions with sewage sludge.
McBee et al. (1) and Eaton et al. (2) have indicated mirex pyrolysis occurs only at temperatures above 500°. Holloman et al.
(10) found that at 700° the major pyrolysis product of mirex was
hexachlorobenzene. It was the object of this reseach to determine
whether mirex residues in shipment containers could be reduced to
acceptable levels by combinations of chemical extraction, chemical
degradation, or pyrolysis.

I $R_1=R_2=R_3=R_4=Cl$
II $R_1=H$, $R_2=R_3=R_4=Cl$
III $R_3=H$, $R_1=R_2=R_4=Cl$
IV $R_1=R_2=H$, $R_3=R_4=Cl$
V $R_3=R_4=H$, $R_1=R_2=Cl$

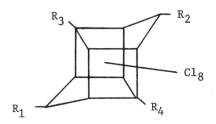

0-8412-0433-0/78/47-073-112$05.00/0

Pyrolysis of Mirex and Its Derivatives

The photochemical ($\underline{4}$, $\underline{5}$) and reductive dechlorination ($\underline{7}$) studies indicated the major products of mirex degradation are 1,2,3,4,5,5,6,7,8,9,10 undecachloropentacyclo [$5.3.0.0^{2,6}.0^{3,9}.0^{4,8}$] decane (II); 1,2,3,4,5,5,6,7,9,10,10 undecachloropentacyclo [$5.3.0.0^{2,6}.0^{3,9}.0^{4,8}$] decane (III); 1,2,3,4,5,6,7,8,9,10 decachloropentacyclo [$5.3.0.0^{2,6}.0^{3,9}.0^{4,8}$] decane (IV); and 1,3,4,5, 5,6,7,9,10,10 decachloropentacyclo [$5.3.0.0^{2,6}.0^{3,9}.0^{4,8}$] decane (V). The pyrolysis of these compounds and mirex were studied at various temperatures and the results of these experiments are given in Tables 1, 2, 3, 4, and 5. After mirex was placed in glass ampules, the ampules were evacuated to 0.5 mm Hg pressure and sealed. These sealed ampules were then placed in a furnace. As shown in Table 1, the mirex started to react at 490° giving both hexachlorobenzene and hexachlorocyclopentadiene. At 600° the mirex gave high yields of hexachlorobenzene.

When heated to 493°, the monohydrogen derivatives of mirex, compounds II and III, produced some hexachlorobenzene and hexachlorocyclopentadiene but also yielded some carbonaceous material (Tables 2 and 3). The 5,10-dihydrogen derivative, compound IV, yielded even more carbonaceous material when heated to 493° (Table 5) than the monohydrogen derivatives.

At 493° the 2,8-dihydrogen derivative of mirex produced predominately carbonaceous material and no materials which were soluble in carbon disulfide.

Since mirex and three of its derivatives all produced hexachlorobenzene, very little information was obtained about the mechanism of the pyrolysis reaction. However, it was observed that pyrolysis of mirex yielded hexachlorocyclopentadiene before the hexachlorobenzene was formed. To test this hypothesis further, hexachlorocyclopentadiene was heated at temperatures ranging from 493° to 550° (Table 6). At the highest temperature (550°) and at longer reaction times the hexachlorobenzene was formed.

Table 1

Pyrolysis of Mirex

Temp. C°	Time Min.	Products	Ratio	Remarks
475	15	Mirex		No Carbon
490	15	Mirex, C_6Cl_6, C_5Cl_6	10:10:1	No Carbon
493	30	C_6Cl_6, C_5Cl_6	1:0.65	No Mirex No Carbon
600	30	C_6Cl_6, C_5Cl_6	1:0.06	No Carbon

Table 2

Pyrolysis 10-Hydrogen Mirex

Temp. C^o	Time Min.	Products	Ratio	Remarks
400	15	10-H, C_5Cl_6	5:1	Light Carbon
481	2	C_5Cl_6		Light Carbon
493	5	C_5Cl_6, C_6Cl_6 (trace)		Medium Carbon
493	30	C_5Cl_6, C_6Cl_6	1:6	Heavy Carbon

Table 3

Pyrolysis of 8-Hydrogen Mirex

Temp. C^o	Time Min.	Products	Ratio	Remarks
400	60	8-H	Low Yield	Heavy Carbon
490	60	8-H	Low Yield	Heavy Carbon
493	30	C_6Cl_6	Good Yield	Light Carbon

Table 4

Pyrolysis of 5,10-Dihydrogen Mirex

Temp. C^o	Time Min.	Products	Ratio	Remarks
400	60	5,10 diH	Low Yield	Heavy Carbon
420	60	5,10 diH	Low Yield	Heavy Carbon
493	30	C_5Cl_6, C_6Cl_6	1:16	Heavy Carbon
493	60	C_6Cl_6		Heavy Carbon

Table 5

Pyrolysis of 2,8-Dihydrogen Mirex

Temp. C^o	Time Min.	Products	Ratio	Remarks
465	2	Carbon		No soluble products
493	30	Carbon		No soluble products

Table 6

Pyrolysis of Hexachlorocyclopentadiene

Temp. C°	Time Min.	Products	Ratio	Remarks
493	10	C_5Cl_6, C_6Cl_6	1:1	
500	5	C_5Cl_6		Oxygen
500	5	C_5Cl_6		Nitrogen
520	5	C_5Cl_6		Nitrogen
550	5	C_5Cl_6, C_6Cl_6	1:5	Nitrogen
550	5	C_6Cl_6		Oxygen

Chemical Extraction

Another study was designed to determine whether solvent extraction techniques could be devised to lower the mirex residues in the drums to an acceptable level. Hexane was chosen to extract the plastic liners because many other solvents such as methylene chloride and tetrahydrofuran attack the plastic. A simple rinsing of the barrel and the plastic liners (1 ml/60 cm²) with hexane removed less than 15% of the mirex residue (Table 7). The percent decontamination was based on the total amount of mirex which would be extracted in 24 hours in a Soxhlet extractor using hexane as the solvent. A rapid immersion of the drum in methylene chloride and the liners in hexane (Table 8) removed much more mirex (81-99%), but the results varied too much to be acceptable. A single five minute immersion of the liners (Table 9) in hexane removed 95-98% of the mirex. A second immersion brought the total decontamination to 99 to 99.9% for the liners. This technique was not satisfactory for decontaminating the fiber drums since four immersions were necessary to remove 81% of the mirex. A comparison of Tables 8 and 9 indicates that methylene chloride is much more efficient for extracting the fiber drums than is hexane.

Conclusion

Chemical degradation and a combination of chemical degradation and incineration in a standard incinerator were found to be unsatisfactory methods for decontaminating the shipment cartons. Extraction of the mirex from the drums and liners were deemed possible but expensive. Alternative solutions to the problem are (a) burn the drums and liners in an incinerator capable of decontaminating mirex (b) return cartons to the manufacturer for reuse.

Table 7

Removal of Mirex from Shipping Containers

Hexane Rinse

Rinse (1ml/60cm^2)	Barrel ppm (% removal)	Inner Bag ppm (% removal)	Middle Bag ppm (% removal)	Outside Bag ppm (% removal)
1	1.24(0.4)	3,650(11)	175(4.7)	172(4.7)
2	0.25(0.5)	370(12)	26(5.4)	24(6.4)
3	0.05(0.5)	129(13)	11(5.7)	15(6.8)
4	0(0.5)	28(13)	11(6.0)	11(6.1)

Soxhlet Extractor (Hexane)

Barrel	Inner Bag	Middle Bag	Outside Bag
300 ppm	32,000 ppm	3,700 ppm	3,600 ppm

*Cumulative percent based on Soxhlet Extraction

Table 8

Removal of Mirex from Shipping
Containers by Immersion in a Solvent

Wash (1.5ml/cm^4)	Barrel (methylene chloride)	Inner Bag (hexane)	Middle Bag (hexane)	Outside Bag (hexane)
1	300 ppm	21,000 ppm	4,000 ppm	3,700 ppm
2		2,500 ppm	520 ppm	700 ppm

Table 9

Removal of Mirex from Shipping Containers
by Soaking in Hexane for 5 Minutes

Soak (1ml/cm^2)	Barrel ppm (%)	Inner Bag ppm (%)	Middle Bag ppm (%)	Outside Bag ppm (%)
1	400(47)	35,000(98)	2,300(97)	3,300(95)
2	100(58)	670(99.9)	50(99)	170(99.8)
3	60(64)	30(99.9)	17(99.9)	4.3(99.9)
4	150(81)	13(99.9)	1(99.7)	0.4(99.9)
Extraction (4 hrs.)	163	0.5	5.4	0.9

Literature Cited

1. McBee, E. T., Roberts, C. W., Idol, J. D., Jr., Earle, R.
H., Jr., J. Amer. Chem. (1956), Soc. 78, 1511.
2. Eaton, P., Carlson, E., Lombardo, P., Yates, P., J. Org.
Chem. (1960), 25, 1225.
3. Dilling, W. L., Braendlin, H. P., McBee, E. T., Tetrahedron
(1967), 23, 1211.
4. Alley, E. G., Dollar, D. A., Layton, B. R., Minyard, J. P.,
Jr., J. Agric. Food Chem. (1973), 21, 138.
5. Alley, E. G., Layton, B. R., Minyard, J. P., Jr., J. Agric.
Food Chem. (1974), 22, 727.
6. Gibson, J. R., Ivie, G. W., Dorough, H. W., J. Agric. Food
Chem. (1972), 20, 1246.
7. Holmstead, R., J. Agric. Food Chem. (1976), 24, 620.
8. Andrade, P. S. L., Jr., Wheeler, W. B., Bull. Environ.
Contam. Toxicol. (1974), 11, 415.
9. Ivie, G. W., Dorough, H. W., Alley, E. G., J. Agric. Food
Chem. (1974), 22, 933.
10. Holloman, M. E., Layton, B. R., Kennedy, M. V., Swanson,
C. R., J. Agric. Food Chem. (1975), 23, 1011.

MARCH 23, 1978

10

Destruction of Pesticides and Pesticide Containers by Molten Salt Combustion

S. J. YOSIM, K. M. BARCLAY, and L. F. GRANTHAM

Rockwell International, Atomics International Division, 8900 DeSoto Avenue, Canoga Park, CA 91304

The disposal of hazardous wastes such as pesticides is receiving increasing attention. Alternate methods to the traditional means of disposal (including open dumping, discharge into rivers, lakes, and oceans, sanitary landfills, and conventional incineration) are being sought.

This paper presents some experimental results which demonstrate the feasibility of applying molten salt combustion technology to the disposal of pesticides and their containers. The concept of molten salt combustion is described first. This is followed by a description of the molten salt combustors used at Atomics International. Then some results of molten salt combustion tests on pesticides and pesticide container material are given. A brief description of a portable unit for this application concludes the paper.

Concept of Molten Salt Combustion

In the Atomics International concept for molten salt combustion, shown in Figure 1, combustible material and air are continuously introduced beneath the surface of a molten salt. The combustible material is added in such a manner that any gas formed during combustion is forced to pass through the melt before it is emitted into the atmosphere. The off-gas contains carbon dioxide, steam, nitrogen, and unreacted oxygen. This gas is cleaned of particulates by scrubbing in a venturi scrubber or by passing it through a baghouse. The heating value of the waste is, in general, sufficient to generate enough heat to heat the reactants to the required temperature, maintain the salt in the molten state, and balance all heat losses from the system.

Ash and other noncombustible materials build up in the melt and must be removed. In certain applications with low throughput, the salt-ash mixture is removed batchwise and discarded. When the throughput is sufficiently large, a side stream of the melt is withdrawn either batchwise or continuously and is processed. The ash must be removed to preserve the fluidity of the

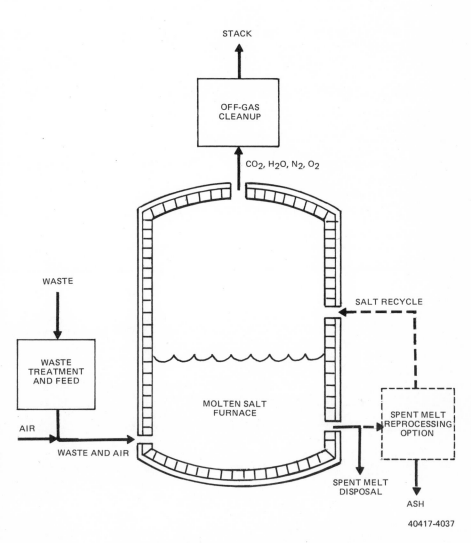

Figure 1. Molten salt combustion process concept

melt at an ash concentration of about 20 wt %. The spent melt is first quenched in water. The solution is then filtered to remove the ash and processed to convert soluble impurities to disposable products. The regenerated salt is then recycled to the combustor.

A hydraulic aqueous simulation of the air-sparged molten salt combustor is shown in Figure 2. In this simulator, concentrated aqueous zinc chloride is used. The intimate contact of the air and liquid can be seen. This intimate contact in the case of a molten salt plus the intimate contact of both fluids with combustible material provide for complete and rapid destruction of such material.

Molten sodium carbonate containing 10 wt % sodium sulfate is the salt used for combustion. Sodium carbonate is used because it is alkaline and reacts instantly with acidic gases such as HCl (produced from organic chloride compounds) and SO_2 (from organic sulfur compounds). The sodium sulfate catalyzes the combustion rate of carbon. This salt system which operates at 800 to 1000°C is stable, nonvolatile, inexpensive, and nontoxic. The chemical reactions of the waste with salt and air depend on its constituents. The carbon and hydrogen of the waste are converted to CO_2 and steam, respectively. The halogens form the corresponding sodium halide salts. The phosphorus, sulfur, arsenic, and silicon (from glass or ash in the waste) form the oxygenated salts, Na_3PO_4, Na_2SO_4, $NaAsO_3$, and Na_2SiO_3, respectively. The iron from metal containers forms iron oxide. The temperatures of combustion are too low to permit a significant amount of nitrogen oxides to be formed by fixation of the nitrogen in the air. The ash is trapped in the melt. At the operating temperatures above 800°C, odor and infectious material are completely destroyed.

Molten Salt Combustion Facilities

There are two molten salt combustion facilities at Atomics International. One is a bench-scale molten salt combustor for disposing of 1/2 to 2 lb/h of waste. Feasibility and optimizing tests are generally carried out in this combustor. The other is a pilot plant combustor, capable of disposing of 50 to 200 lb/h of waste, and is used to obtain engineering data for reliable extrapolation to a full-scale plant.

Bench-Scale Molten Salt Combustor. A schematic of the bench-scale molten salt combustor is shown in Figure 3. Approximately 12 lb of molten salt are contained in a 6-in. ID and 30-in. high alumina tube placed in a Type 321 stainless steel retainer vessel. This stainless steel vessel, in turn, is contained in an 8-in. ID, four heating zone Marshall furnace. The four heating zones are each 8 in. in height, and the temperature of each zone is controlled by an SCR controller. Furnace and reactor temperatures are recorded by a 12-point Barber-Colman chart recorder.

Figure 2. Hydraulic simulation of air-sparged molten salt

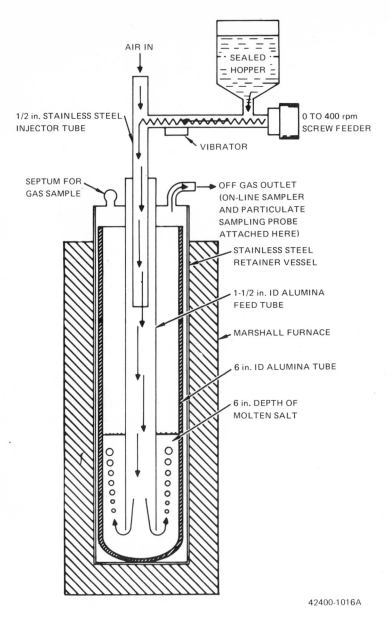

Figure 3. Bench-scale molten salt combustor

Solids, pulverized in a No. 4 Wiley mill to <1 mm in particle size, are metered into the 1/2-in. OD central tube of the injector by a screw feeder. Rotation of the screw feeder is provided by a 0 to 400-rpm Eberback Corporation Con-Torque stirrer motor. In the injector, the solids are mixed with the air being used for gasification, and this solids-air mixture passes downward through the center tube of the injector and emerges into the 1-1/2-in. ID alumina feed tube. This alumina feed tube is adjusted so that its end is 1/2 in. above the bottom of the 6-in. diameter alumina reactor tube. Thus, the solids-air mixture is forced to pass downward through the feed tube, outward at its bottom end, and then upward through 6 in. of salt in the annulus between the 1-1/2-in. and the 6-in. alumina tubes. In the case of liquids, a different feed system is used. The liquid is pumped with a laboratory pump and is sprayed into the alumina feed tube.

Pilot-Scale Molten Salt Combustor. Photographs of the molten salt pilot combustor and some of the auxiliary components are shown in Figures 4 and 5, respectively.

The molten salt vessel, 10 ft high and 3 ft ID, is made of Type 304 stainless steel, and is lined with 6-in.-thick refractory blocks. It contains 1 ton of salt, which corresponds to a depth of 3 ft, with no air flow through the bed. The vessel is preheated on startup and kept hot on standby by a natural-gas-fired burner.

The salt loading is fed into the molten salt vessel through the carbonate feeder. The combustible materials to be processed are transferred directly from the hammermill, in which they are crushed to the required size, into a feed hopper provided with a variable-speed auger, and then introduced into the air stream for transport into the vessel.

The exhaust gases generated in the vessel exit through refractory-lined tubes in the vessel head to a refractory-lined mist separator. The separator traps entrained melt droplets on a baffle assembly. The gases are then ducted to a high-energy venturi scrubber or to a baghouse, which is used to remove any particulate matter before release to the atmosphere. An overflow weir permits continuous removal of spent salt, thus permitting long-term tests to be carried out.

Results of Combustion Tests

The container materials tested included those that were combustible (paper, plastic, and rubber) as well as noncombustible (glass and metal). The pesticides which were tested included DDT, malathion, chlordane, and 2,4D.

Container Materials. A summary chart giving the results of combustion tests in the bench-scale unit with paper, plastic, rubber, and a blend of these wastes is shown in Table I. Combustion was complete in all cases. The CO ($\leq 0.2\%$), NO_x

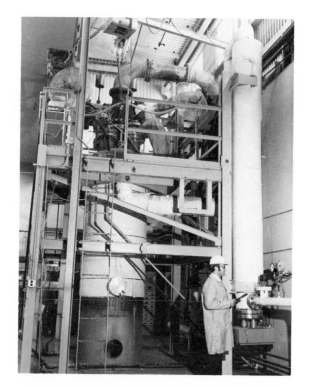

Figure 4.   Pilot-scale molten salt combustor

TABLE I

SUMMARY CHART — MOLTEN SALT COMBUSTION OF COMBUSTIBLE
CONTAINER MATERIALS

Waste Material	Feed Rate (lb/h)	Air Feed Rate* (scfm)	Tempera-ture (°C)	Effluent Analysis				
				CO (%)	CO_2 (%)	NO_x (ppm)	Hydrocarbons as N-Hexane (ppm)	Particulates[†] (grains/scf)
Paper	1.6	5	980	0.05	8.3	13	<25	0.03
Plastic (50% PVC - 50% PE)	1.1	5	960	0.1	11.9	18	<25	0.24
Rubber	0.7	5	982	0.05	8.3	62	<25	0.35
Blend (60% Paper, 30% Plastic, 10% Rubber)	1.5	5	960	0.05	10.7	27	<25	0.14

*The gas superficial velocity was 2 ft/s.
†The bench-scale unit was not designed to maintain low particulate emission.

(<65 ppm), and unburned hydrocarbons (<30 ppm) concentrations in the off-gas were very low. No HCl was detected in the tests with PVC. The particulate loading in the off-gas was rather low considering that no particulate removal device was present in the bench-scale combustor.

Combustion tests on 1500 lb of simulated pesticide containers were performed in the pilot combustor at feed rates of 70 lb/h. The waste contained paper, polyethylene, PVC, and rubber. The results are shown in Table II. No HCl (<5 ppm), SO_2 (<2 ppm), CO (<0.1%), or hydrocarbons (<0.1%) were detected. The NO_x concentration was about 30 ppm.

TABLE II

OFF-GAS ANALYSIS FOR COMBUSTION OF
SIMULATED PESTICIDE CONTAINERS
IN PILOT PLANT

1500 lb of Waste Burned at 70-lb/h Rate

Waste Contained Paper, Polyethylene, PVC and Rubber

Off-Gas Analysis:

HCl	ND[*]	(<5 ppm)
SO_2	ND	(<2 ppm)
CO	ND	(<0.1%
HC	ND	(<0.1%)
NO_x	30 ppm	
O_2	5-12%	
CO_2	10-15%	
N_2	76-78%	

*ND — Not Detected

The reaction rate of glass with melt was moderate at 900°C (complete in about 30 min) and was rapid at 1000°C. At 1000°C, the glass reacted as rapidly as it was added. The reaction rate, in the case of metal, was considerably slower. Surface corrosion of about 70 mils took place in 8 h at 900°C. While the reaction rate is expected to be significantly higher at 1000°C, it is not recommended that molten salts be used to completely disintegrate metal containers. Another option is to immerse the containers for several minutes in the melt for a decontamination rinse only.

Pesticides.   Typical combustion results with DDT and malathion performed in the bench-scale unit are shown in Table III.
The melts contained either Na$_2$CO$_3$ or K$_2$CO$_3$. The use of
K$_2$CO$_3$ is of interest because the combustion product, KCl, can
be used as a fertilizer. Destruction of the pesticide was greater
than 99.99%.· No pesticides were detected in the melt; however,
traces of pesticides were detected in the off-gas. The last two
columns of Table III compare the concentration of pesticide in
the off-gas with threshold limit values (TLV). (The TLV's refer
to airborne concentrations of substances and represent conditions under which it is believed that nearly all workers may be
repeatedly exposed, day after day, without adverse effect.) The
concentrations of pesticides in the off-gas were generally well
below the TLV. This comparison is a conservative one since
the off-gas will be considerably diluted when it reaches the
worker area. Another consideration is the fact that in these
tests, a 6-in.-deep salt bed was used. In an actual disposal
plant, a 36-in.-deep salt bed is expected to be used. This will
increase the residence time and contact time by a factor of 6;
therefore, the extent of destruction of these pesticides is expected to exceed considerably the 99.99%+ found in the laboratory
tests.·

The herbicide 2,4D (an ester of dichlorophenoxyacetic acid)
was of interest because it was an actual waste which contained
30 to 50% 2,4D, and 50 to 70% tars (mostly bis-ester and di-
chlorophenol tars). The waste, which was rather viscous, was
diluted by the addition of 1/4 its weight with ethanol. The destruction of the herbicide at 830°C was >99.98%; no organic
chlorides or HCl were detected in the melt or in the exhaust gas.
(In this case, a less sensitive analytical technique was used.)

Earlier tests were performed with chlordane. No chlordane
was detected in the off-gas. Greater than 99.96% of the pesticide was destroyed.

The effectiveness of sodium carbonate in preventing HCl
emissions was determined. In this test, trichloroethane
(C$_2$H$_3$Cl$_3$), which contains 80 wt % Cl, was combusted to determine how much of the Na$_2$CO$_3$ could be converted into NaCl and
still be present in sufficient amount to prevent HCl emissions.
Prevention of HCl emissions was accomplished with as little as
2 wt % Na$_2$CO$_3$. No trichloroethane (<0.001% of the material
fed) could be detected in the off-gas.

Conceptual Study of a Portable Molten Salt Disposal System

A conceptual and preliminary design for a portable molten
salt unit for disposal of emptied pesticide containers was completed. An artist's concept is shown in Figure 6, which shows a
combustor and the auxiliary components mounted on a truck bed.
The combustor, which is a 6-ft ID and 11 ft tall, is capable of

Figure 5.   Feed system for the molten salt test facility

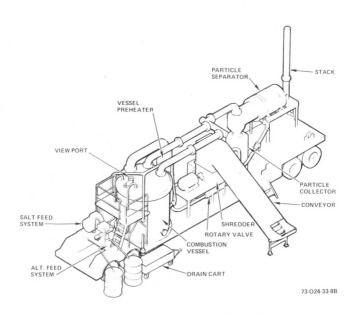

73-024-33-8B

Figure 6.   Portable molten salt waste disposal system

TABLE III

TYPICAL RESULTS OF COMBUSTION TESTS ON MALATHION AND DDT

Pesticide	Salt	Average Test Temperature (°C)	Percent Pesticide Destroyed	Concentration of Pesticide in Melt (ppm)	Quantity in Exhaust Gas (mg/m³)	TLV* of Pesticide (mg/m³)
DDT	Na_2CO_3	922	99.997	ND† <0.05	1.4	1
DDT	K_2CO_3	894	99.998	ND <0.2	0.3	1
Malathion	Na_2CO_3	922	99.996	ND <0.01	1.1	15
Malathion	K_2CO_3	896	99.999	ND <0.005	ND <0.4	15

*Threshold Limit Value
†Not Detected

processing 500 lb/h of waste. The waste containers are transferred by conveyor to a shredder, which produces 1-1/4-in. to
3/8-in. particles. The shredded material is pneumatically con-
veyed to the combustor. The off-gas is cleaned by a particle
separator to remove the larger entrained particles and then is
cleaned by a baghouse (not shown) before it is emitted from the
stack. With such a unit, a ton of empty paper containers results
in only 1/3 yd^3 of spent salt. The spent salt is drained into a
drain cart and buried in a Class 1 dump. The system is cooled
and then moved to a new site where fresh salt would be added to
the combustor and the cycle repeated.

Advantages of Molten Salt Combustion

The advantages of molten salt combustion for the disposal of
pesticide wastes are:

1) Intimate contact of the hot melt, air, and waste provides
   for complete and immediate destruction of the hazardous
   material.

2) No acidic gaseous pollutants, e. g. , HCl from chlorinated
   compounds such as DDT and chlordane and H_2S or SO_2
   from sulfur-containing compounds such as malathion, are
   emitted.

3) Combustion products are sterile and odor-free.

4) Sodium carbonate is stable, nonvolatile, inexpensive,
   and nontoxic.

5) The process is applicable for a great variety of other
   wastes. These include chemical warfare agents, hazardous industrial wastes, hospital wastes, carcinogenic
   materials, and low-level radioactive wastes.

MARCH 23, 1978

Binding and Release of Insecticide Residues in Soils

T. W. FUHREMANN, E. P. LICHTENSTEIN, and J. KATAN[1]

Department of Entomology, University of Wisconsin, Madison, WI 53706

This paper summarizes data obtained recently in our laboratory and deals with the subject of soil-bound insecticide
residues (1,2,3,4,5).
Due to potential hazards to living organisms, some of the
more persistent insecticides have been replaced by less persistent compounds which seem to rapidly "disappear" from environmental components, such as soil. For many years depletion
curves indicating the persistence or rate of disappearance
of insecticides applied to soils have been published. Typical
depletion curves (figure 1) were obtained in 1964 by our group
after applying insecticides at the same rate, the same time and
by the same methods to loam soil field plots near Madison, WI
(6). These depletion curves indicated that compounds like aldrin
or dieldrin persist in soil considerably longer than malathion,
methylparathion or parathion. Frequently the decline in detectable residues has been associated with such terms as "disappearance", "loss" or "volatilization". However, the apparent disappearance of a pesticide from soil can be due to our inability
to detect it's residues by conventional procedures. One reason
a chemical cannot be detected is that the compound or its degradation products cannot be extracted from soil, thus they are
'invisible'. Those residues which can be extracted long after
their application are the 'visible', persistent ones.
The use of radiolabeled pesticides in laboratory studies
has made it possible to detect unextractable soil residues.
Combustion or strong hydrolysis of extracted soils can release
these unextracted or bound ^{14}C-residues. The problem of these
bound residues, however, is complicated since present methods
for their release or liberation also result in the destruction
or their identity. Insight into the mechanism of binding of
pesticide residues to soils might shed some light on the nature
of the residues and their potential release.
Utilizing ^{14}C-ring labelled parathion, the amount of unextractable or bound ^{14}C-residues in a sandy and a loam soil were
determined by combustion to $^{14}CO_2$, after the soils had been

0-8412-0433-0/78/47-073-131$05.00/0
© 1978 American Chemical Society

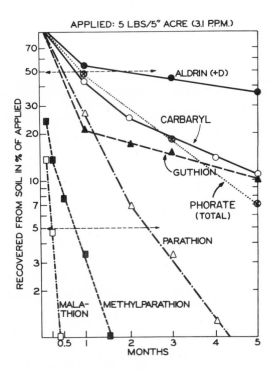

Figure 1. Depletion curves depicting extractable residues of various insecticides applied at 6 kg/ha (concentration, 3.1 ppm) to loam soils in field plots

extracted 3 times with benzene-acetone-methanol (1:1:1) (1).
Depletion curves of extractable parathion residues established
during a 1-month incubation period (figure 2) were similar to
those established under field conditions and resulted finally in
recoveries of 30 to 36% of the insecticide dose applied to the
loam soil. With a steady decrease of extractable residues
over a 1-month incubation period, an increase of unextractable,
bound ^{14}C-residues occurred. This resulted finally in total
recoveries of extracted plus bound residues, which amounted to
80% of the applied radiocarbon. Attempts to exhaustively extract these bound ^{14}C-residues with a variety of solvents
ranging in polarity from benzene to water failed to further
extract a significant amount. The rate of binding of ^{14}C-
residues was highest in the loam soil and was related to the
activity of soil microorganiams. In soils, sterilized by gamma
irradiation or by autoclaving, the binding of ^{14}C-parathion was
reduced by 58 to 84%. Under anaerobic conditions, created by
flooding soils with water, the rate of binding of ^{14}C-compounds
doubled. The amount of bound residues decreased from 67% to 16%
when soils had been sterilized prior to the insecticide treatment
and flooding. Reinoculation of this soil with microorganisms
fully reinstated the soil binding capacity. Incubation of the
moist treated soil under nitrogen also increased the formation
of bound residues, while incubation at 6°C rather than 27°C
inhibited binding. When these experiments were repeated using
^{14}C-ethyl rather than ^{14}C-ring labelled parathion, identical
results were obtained which indicates that the bound residues
apparently contain both the aryl and alkyl portions of the
parathion molecule. This information led us to suspect that
amino-parathion which contains both the aryl and alkyl portions
of the molecule and is formed under anaerobic conditions, might
be the bound residue. In addition, data from our laboratory
published in 1964 (7) indicated that while parathion residues
could be extracted and detected by thin-layer chromatography
in loam soil extracts after several weeks of soil incubation,
amino-parathion and p-aminophenol, could not be recovered after
a 1 day soil incubation. When this experiment was repeated in
1976 using radiolabeled compounds we found that 49% of applied
^{14}C-aminoparathion could not be extracted from the soil 2 hours
after its application, while only 1.6% of applied parathion
was bound in 2 hours (2). Comparison of binding of all the
nitro and amino analogs of parathion (figure 3) during a brief
2 hour incubation with loam soil indicated that in all cases
the amino compounds were bound to a much greater extent than
the nitro-compounds.

The role of microorganisms in producing ^{14}C-parathion
derived bound residues and the mechanism of production of soil
bound residues was also investigated by incubating ^{14}C-ring-
parathion in soil-free culture media that had been inoculated
with soil microorganisms (2). The amounts of ^{14}C-compounds

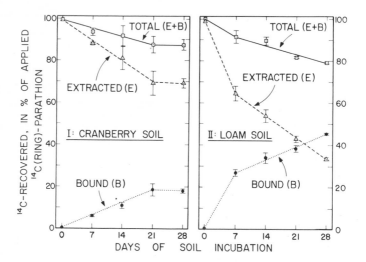

Figure 2. Binding and extractability of ^{14}C-ring-parathion in two soils during a 28-day incubation period at 27°C (applied dose, 1 ppm). The amounts of parathion as determined by GLC in the loam soil extract were nearly identical to its radiocarbon content. (I) Sandy soil from cranberry bog; (II) loam soil. Curve B, bound parathion; Curve E, extracted parathion; and Curve E + B, the total.

in culture supernatants, that upon addition to soil became unextractable, increased up to 12 hours of microbial culture
incubation, when 43% of the applied radiocarbon was bound after
a 2-hour soil incubation period (figure 4). The increase in
soil bound residues was correlated with a decrease in the amount
of parathion in the microbial culture and a concomitant increase
in the appearance of the major degradation product, aminoparathion (figure 5).

   These data indicate that the production of soil bound
residues of parathion occurs in two steps. First microorganisms
convert parathion to aminoparathion and then this amino-parathion
becomes rapidly bound to soil. These soil bound residues are
unextractable and therefore not detected in routine residue
analyses.

   Experiments conducted with ^{14}C-phorate ($\underline{3}$) indicated that
26.4% of the applied residues had become soil-bound within one
week of incubation. Contrary to results with ^{14}C-parathion,
binding of ^{14}C-phorate residues did not increase after 1 week.
Further investigations ($\underline{4}$) pertaining to the extractability
and formation of bound ^{14}C-residues in an agricultural loam
soil were conducted with the "non-persistent" insecticides
^{14}C-methylparathion and ^{14}C-fonofos (Dyfonate ^{R}) and with the
"persistent" insecticides ^{14}C-dieldrin and ^{14}C-p,p'-DDT (figure
6). With ^{14}C-methylparathion only 7% of the applied radiocarbon
was extractable 28 days after soil treatment, while ^{14}C-bound
residues amounted to 43% of the applied dose.

   Field studies conducted in 1968-69 indicated that fonofos
has a half-life in Plano silt loam soil under Wisconsin summer
conditions of about 28 days ($\underline{8}$). In the laboratory this loam
soil was treated with ^{14}C-ring or ^{14}C-ethyl labelled fonofos
and incubated for various periods. After 28 days about 47%
of the radiocarbon was extractable and most of this was
fonofos. However, unextractable ^{14}C-residues increased with
incubation time resulting after 4 weeks in 35% of the applied
residues being soil bound. These residues were of course not
detected in the field study. Results using ^{14}C-ring or ^{14}C-
ethyl labelled fonofos were very similar indicating that the
bound residues probably don't involve a cleavage product. Contrary to results obtained with parathion the binding of fonofos
does not appear to be dependent on microbial activity. While
irradiation or autoclaving soil prior to insecticide treatment
and incubation significantly reduced the binding of parathion
and flooding enhanced it, fonofos binding was not reduced by
irradiation. Autoclaving reduced binding somewhat, possibly
due to an alteration of soil structure and flooding slightly
reduced fonofos binding. Smaller amounts of soil-bound residues
had been formed with the "persistent" insecticides amounting
after 28 days to only 6.5% of the applied ^{14}C-dieldrin and to
25% of the applied ^{14}C-p,p'-DDT, while 95% and 72%, respectively
were still recovered by organic solvent extraction.

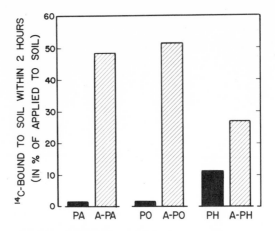

Figure 3.   Amounts of ^{14}C-bound residues in soils, 2 hr after soil treatment at 1 ppm with ^{14}C-parathion (PA), ^{14}C-aminoparathion (A–PA), ^{14}C-paraoxon (PO), ^{14}C-aminoparaoxon (A–PO), p-^{14}C-nitrophenol (PH), or p-^{14}C-aminophenol (A–PH)

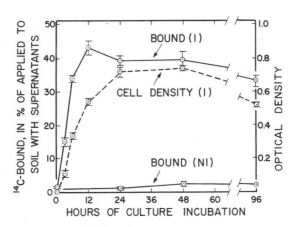

Figure 4.   Binding of ^{14}C compounds to soil within 2 hr after the addition of supernatants obtained from 0–96-hr old microbial cultures, treated with ^{14}C-parathion and inoculated (I) with soil microorganisms; NI = noninoculated controls

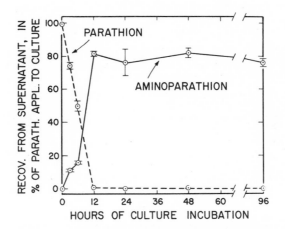

Figure 5. Amounts of parathion and amino-para-thion determined by gas liquid chromatography in benzene extracts of supernatants of microbial cultures after treatment with ^{14}C-ring-parathion at 10 ppm and incubation for 0–96 hr

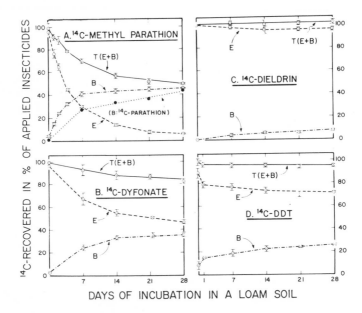

Figure 6. Binding and extractability of ^{14}C-labeled insecticides in a silt loam soil during a 28-day incubation period, after soil treatment at 1 ppm. With the exception of ^{14}C-methylparathion the amounts of extractable ^{14}C-Dyfonate (fonofos), ^{14}C-Dieldrin, and ^{14}C-DDT, as determined by gas–liquid chromatography, were similar to the amounts of extractable radiocarbon. For comparison purposes, data are inserted in A for the bound residues of ^{14}C-parathion in soil. E = extracted; B = bound; T = total of E + B.

They differed from the organophosphorus compounds in their relatively low binding properties and their high extractability from soils.

The question of the potential biological availability of bound insecticide residues was investigated (4) by testing the insecticidal activity of bound residues from ^{14}C-fonofos and ^{14}C-methylparathion treated soils with fruit flies (Drosophila). With soils containing unextractable radiocarbon at the insecticide equivalent of 3 ppm, no mortalities were observed during a 24-hour exposure period to the soil and only slight mortalities occurred during an additional 48-hour exposure period. However, with soils to which the insects were exposed immediately following the insecticide application at the same concentration as the unextractable radiocarbon (3 ppm), 50% of the flies had died within 2-3 hours after fonofos application and within 18-20 hours after soil treatment with methylparathion. It appears, therefore, that bound insecticide residues are not only unextractable, but they are also less active biologically.

Experiments were also conducted to study the release and availability of unextractable, soil-bound residues of ^{14}C-ring-methylparathion and the potential pick up of these ^{14}C-residues by earthworms and oat plants (5). Data from this investigation indicate that unextractable soil-bound insecticide residues are not entirely excluded from environmental interaction. After incubation of soil treated with ^{14}C-methylparathion for 14 days, and exhaustive solvent extractions, bound residues remaining in this soil amounted to 32.5% of the applied insecticide. However, after worms had lived for 2 to 6 weeks in this previously extracted soil containing only bound residues or several crops of oats had grown in it, sizable amounts of ^{14}C-residues were found in these organisms. Earthworms which lived in the soil for 6 weeks contained a total of 2.7% of the ^{14}C-residues which could not be extracted from these soils, while 3 crops of oats plants each grown for 2 weeks contained a total of 5.1%. The majority of previously soil-bound ^{14}C-residues taken up by earthworms (58-66%) again became bound within these worms, while most (82-95%) of the ^{14}C-residues in oat plants were extractable. Greens of oat plants contained 46-62% of the ^{14}C-residues recovered from plants. Most of the ^{14}C-residues in oat greens were benzene-soluble while most of the ^{14}C-residues in the seeds and roots were water-soluble.

Because soil-bound insecticide residues can be released from soil by these organisms any loss in toxicity due to binding should not be regarded as permanent. Even if release of nontoxic compounds occurs, interaction with other chemicals in the environment cannot be disregarded. The release and potential biological activity of these bound residues certainly warrants further study. In view of the above findings, the expression "disappearance" and "persistence" of pesticides, so widely used during the last two decades, should be reassessed to consider the bound products.

Literature Cited

1. Katan, J., Fuhremann, T.W., Lichtenstein, E.P., Science (1976) 193(4256) 891-894.
2. Katan, J., Lichtenstein, E.P., J. Ag. Food Chem. (1977) 25(6) 1404-1408.
3. Lichtenstein, E.P., Liang, T.T., Fuhremann, T.W., J. Ag. Food Chem. (1978) Submitted.
4. Lichtenstein, E.P., Katan, J., Anderegg, B.N., J. Ag. Food Chem. (1977) 25(1) 43-47.
5. Fuhremann, T.W., Lichtenstein, E.P., J. Ag. Food Chem. (1978) In Press.
6. Lichtenstein, E.P., Pure Appl. Chem. (1975) 42(1) 113-118.
7. Lichtenstein, E.P., Schulz, K.R., J. Econ Entomol. (1964) 57(5) 618-627.
8. Schulz, K.R., Lichtenstein, E.P., J. Econ Entomol. (1971) 64(1) 283-287.

Footnotes

[1] Present Address: Hebrew University, Faculty of Agriculture, Rehovot, Israel.
[2] Research supported by the College of Agricultural and Life Sciences, University of Wisconsin, Madison and by grants from the Environmental Protection Agency (R 804920) and the National Science Foundation (DEB76-08869). Contribution by Project 1387 from the Wisconsin Agricultural Experiment Station as a collaborator under North Central Regional Cooperative Research Project 96, entitled "Environmental Implications of Pesticide Usage".

MARCH 23, 1978

Dieldrin Elimination from Animal Tissues

K. L. DAVISON

U.S. Department of Agriculture, S.E.A. Metabolism and Radiation Research
Laboratory, Fargo, ND 58102

In 1974, dieldrin residues above U. S. Food and Drug Administration tolerances for human consumption were discovered in
body fat of turkeys from two flocks in North Dakota. Turkeys
from one of these flocks were used to investigate the effectiveness of phenobarbital for causing the turkeys to eliminate the
dieldrin. Phenobarbital did not cause a detectable change in
the rate of dieldrin elimination but did stimulate our most
recent investigations of dieldrin elimination from animal
tissues.

This report provides a brief review of recent research on
dieldrin elimination from animals and a summary of attempts to
remove dieldrin from chickens and turkeys. A thorough review of
dieldrin accumulation, storage, metabolism and elimination by
animals is not intended.

Brief Review

When ingestion of dieldrin remains constant, storage of
dieldrin in body tissues, predominately adipose tissue, apparently plateaus (1). Presumably, a steady state has occurred,
and excretion of dieldrin or its metabolites equals ingestion.
The time required to reach this steady state was 6 weeks in rats
and 22 to 26 weeks in chickens. A steady state for storage and
excretion probably also occurs for other chlorinated hydrocarbon
insecticides when ingestion remains constant.

Heath and Vandekar (2) showed that fecal elimination of
[^{36}Cl]dieldrin, or its metabolites, was increased in rats during
intermittent periods of starvation. The [^{36}Cl]dieldrin accumulated in adipose tissue of the rats when it was fed to them
before the periods of starvation. In the early 1960s, milk from
a number of Maryland dairy farms contained excessive amounts of
heptachlor. The heptachlor residues were traced to heptachlor-
contaminated forage eaten by the cows. At that time, USDA
officials suggested starvation as a means of removing the
heptachlor residues from the contaminated cattle, but apparently

the idea was not tested.

More recently, Cook and his colleagues at Michigan State University recommended using a combination of charcoal and phenobarbital for removing dieldrin residues from cattle. They observed that charcoal fed concurrently with dieldrin increased the amount of dieldrin eliminated in the feces (3). They also observed that phenobarbital induced hepatic mixed-function oxidases in cattle (4). Cook never conducted controlled experiments with phenobarbital alone for removing dieldrin residues from cattle, but he did try using the combination of phenobarbital and carbon on a farm on which dairy cattle were contaminated with dieldrin (5). The herd was split into two groups. One group was untreated and the other group was treated with both phenobarbital and charcoal. Dieldrin residues were reduced more rapidly in milk from treated cows than in milk from untreated cows.

Phenobarbital is effective in removing dieldrin residues from rats (6) and pigs (7). When fed coincident with dieldrin, charcoal was effective in reducing the amount of dieldrin accumulated in body tissues of rats; but once dieldrin had accumulated in body tissues, charcoal feeding had little effect on reducing these residues (6).

Summary of Research with Chickens and Turkeys

When the dieldrin residues were found in body fat of turkeys in two North Dakota flocks in 1974, the decline in residue levels was followed in one of the flocks. The values obtained fit the equation $Y = 5.34 - 0.187X + 0.00252X^2 - 0.0000114X^3$, where Y is the concentration of dieldrin in body fat in ppm and X is the time in days. The correlation coefficient, R^2, for this equation was 0.989. Correlation coefficients for first-order and quadratic equations were 0.868 and 0.957, respectively. Clearly, in this flock of turkeys, the cubic equation described the change in residue levels with time better than the first-order or quadratic equations. At least two factors affected the residue levels. The first factor was dilution by growth, and the second was dieldrin elimination.

After the discovery of the dieldrin residues in turkeys, research was begun to find ways of eliminating dieldrin residues from chickens and turkeys. Because of high grain prices in 1974, the feeding regimen for turkeys in North Dakota was screenings (primarily seed of green and yellow foxtail) plus a 40% protein, commercial supplement. An experiment (8) was conducted with turkeys raised at North Dakota State University. The turkeys were fed the screenings plus supplement diet used by the turkey growers. Dieldrin was fed in this diet for 5 days to build residues in the bodies of the turkeys, and then removed from the diet. The turkeys were then divided into five groups. One group was the control and was fed the screenings plus supplement diet for 68 days. One group was starved for 5 days and then fed the control diet. Another group was given about 200 mg of sodium barbital per turkey in their drinking water. The 4th group was fed a high fiber diet (33% alfalfa meal in the control diet), and the 5th group was fed a high energy high protein diet. These treatments did not detectably reduce residues below those of the control turkeys.

A second experiment (8) was conducted with turkeys that had been fed dieldrin to build residues in their bodies. These turkeys were divided into two groups. The first group was the control and was fed a normal ration for 61 days. The second group was subjected to three periods of starvation (7, 7 and 4 days) interrupted by periods of feeding (7, 12 and 24 days). Periodic starvation was effective in accelerating the decline in both the concentration of dieldrin in body fat and the total amount of dieldrin in the carcasses of the turkeys.

A series of balance experiments were conducted with chickens (9) and turkeys (10) given dieldrin and [^{14}C]dieldrin. Severe starvation, charcoal, cholestyramine (a resin), probucol (a cholesterol lowering drug), Cholistipol (a resin), imbiber beads (an absorbent), Dowex SBR-Cl resin and Dowex XFS-4022 resin were tested for their ability to accelerate the elimination of dieldrin residues. Severe starvation was effective in lowering dieldrin or [^{14}C]dieldrin residues in either chickens or turkeys. Starvation was effective only if severe enough to reduce the amount of body lipids to 10% or less of the carcass dry matter. Cholestyramine was effective in lowering dieldrin or [^{14}C]dieldrin residues in chickens, but was not effective in turkeys. The other materials tested were not effective in either chickens or turkeys.

<u>Literature Cited</u>

1. Davison, K. L. Bull. Environ. Contam. Toxicol. (1973) <u>10</u>, 16-24.

2. Heath, D. F., and Vandekar, M. Brit. J. Industr. Med. (1964) <u>21</u>, 269-279.

3. Wilson, K. A., and Cook, R. M. J. Agr. Food Chem. (1970) <u>18</u>, 437-440.

4. Cook, R. M., and Wilson, K. A. J. Agr. Food Chem. (1970) <u>18</u>, 441-442.

5. McGuire, J. R. Des Moines Sunday Register (July 20, 1969) p. 1-F.

6. Engebretson, K. A., and Davison, K. L. Bull. Environ. Contam. Toxicol. (1971) <u>6</u>, 391-400.

7. Dobson, R. C., and Baugh, E. R. Bull. Environ. Contam. Toxicol. (1976) <u>16</u>, 567-571.

8. Sell, J. L., Davison, K. L., and Bristol, D. W. Poultry Sci. (1977) <u>56</u>, 2045-2051.

9.   Davison, K. L., and Sell, J. L.   Arch. Environ. Contam.
      Toxicol. (Accepted 1978).
10.   Davison, K. L., and Sell, J. L.   Arch. Environ. Contam.
      Toxicol. (Accepted 1977).

Mention of a trade name, proprietary product, or specific equipment does not constitute a guarantee or warranty by the U. S. Department of Agriculture and does not imply its approval to the exclusion of other products that may be suitable.

MARCH 23, 1978

13

Chlorine–Mercury Interactions in Mercury Derivatives of Poly-Chlorinated Phenols and Other Chlorocarbons

GARY WULFSBERG[1], JOHN GRAVES, JUNE GRIFFITHS, and DON ESSIG

Northland College, Ashland, WI 54806

R. J. C. BROWN

Queen's University, Kingston, Ontario

For some time, we have been interested in the metal derivatives of chlorocarbons, which we have studied especially by the technique of chlorine-35 nuclear quadrupole resonance spectroscopy (NQR). Our spectra to date have often turned up evidence of direct (albeit weak) metal-chlorine interaction (1) (Figure 1), suggesting that, under certain circumstances, chlorocarbons might be able to act as ligands for metals. The primary purpose of this study is to elucidate the nature of this metal-chlorine interaction. However, we also hope that, if we can determine optimum conditions for coordination of chlorocarbons, complexes of metal salts with chlorocarbons may be formed which would show enhanced rates of nucleophilic substitution of chloride by the anion of the metal salt, thus opening another possible route to the degradation of waste chlorocarbon pesticides. (This would, of course, be analogous to the silver-ion catalyzed nucleophilic substitution reactions of alkyl halides.) (2)

Our primary strategy in this study has been to prepare metal derivatives of chlorocarbons having two or more chlorines which are chemically equivalent unless there is a metal-chlorine interaction. As an example from Figure 1, we have prepared metal derivatives of 2,6-dichlorophenol. Intramolecular metal-chlorine interaction will create different electronic environments at the two chlorine atoms. ^{35}Cl NQR is very sensitive to such differences, and it may be predicted (1) that the NQR frequency of the interacting chlorine will be lower than the frequency of the normal chlorine. The degree to which the two frequencies are split should reflect approximately the strength of the interaction in the ground state, as long as the interaction is much weaker than the C-Cl bond strength.

A frequency splitting of less than 2%, however, is not reliable evidence of such an interaction: NQR is done on crystalline solids, and in crystal lattices the effects of the electrons in neighboring molecules can vary the observed NQR frequencies by up to 2% in covalent molecules. As the NQR frequencies of the chlorocarbons under study scan the range 34–40 MHz, we take any

---

[1] Current address: Chemistry Department, St. John's University, Collegeville, MN 56321

0-8412-0433-0/78/47-073-145$05.00/0

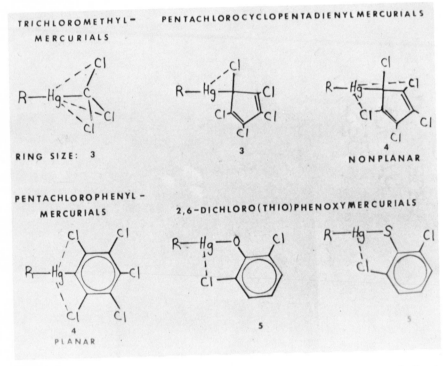

Figure 1. Types of mercury derivatives of chlorocarbons studied in this work. Possible chlorine–mercury interactions are indicated by broken lines (_____), and the size of ring produced by such an interaction is indicated by the number below each figure.

frequency lowering of more than 0.8 MHz as an indicator of an interaction of that chlorine with another atom besides the carbon to which it is bound.

The first part of our study, which is essentially complete, considers the geometrical requirements of the interaction. An intramolecular interaction would complete a "ring" within the molecule, and we might expect that some sizes of rings would be preferred to others. In the solid state, intermolecular interactions may also occur. Extended, weak intermolecular interactions should be weakened by expanding the lattice, as by warming the crystal or reducing the pressure on it. These experiments, we would expect, would reduce the splitting of the NQR frequencies of the two chlorines in our molecule, if the interaction is intermolecular. We expect no consistent effect on the splitting if the interaction is intramolecular.

We have studied the variable-temperature and occasionally the variable-pressure NQR spectra of the mercury derivatives of the classes of chlorocarbons shown in Figure 1. Indicated below each of the drawings is the size of ring expected if intramolecular interaction occurs.

Figure 2 shows the results for the trichloromethylmercurials, $RHgCCl_3$, and for some organic trichloromethanes as models. The observed frequencies were each subtracted from the highest frequency (which is presumably that of a non-interacting chlorine) to give the splittings indicated along the abscissa. Most splittings of the NQR frequencies of the model compounds are small (less than 0.8 MHz). On changing the temperature of NQR measurement from 77 K to room temperature, there is no consistent change in these splittings. (This is indicated along the vertical axis.) A number of mercurials, however, show splittings of greater than 0.8 MHz, which suggests the presence of a chlorine-mercury interaction. Such large splittings are consistently reduced at room temperature, which suggests that intermolecular chlorine-mercury interactions are being observed. A variable-pressure NQR measurement on bis(trichloromethyl)mercury gives results which are also consistent with this suggestion--the splitting is increased by increasing the pressure.

A crystal structure has been reported (6) for one of these mercurials (trichloromethylmercury bromide), but the data on Hg...Cl nonbonded distances can be interpreted in different ways with respect to interactions. (1)

In Figure 3 (closed circles) are shown results for a series of organic derivatives of 2,6-dichlorophenol, and 2,6-dichlorothiophenol. Only crystal lattice splittings should be present; consistent with this all splittings are less than 0.8 MHz--indeed they are less than 0.4 MHz. There is no systematic effect of temperature on these splittings.

The triangles in Figure 3 represent data of Kravstov et al (8) for a number of 4-substituted 2,6-dichlorophenols. Hydrogen bonding is known to occur in this type of compound, and involves

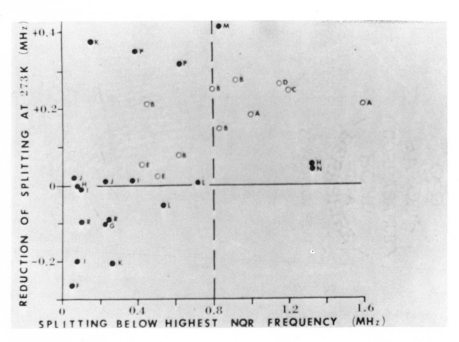

Figure 2. NQR frequency splittings for trichloromethyl compounds at 77K compared with the reduction of these splittings at 273K. (In many cases this splitting is extrapolated, as the frequencies fade out below 273K.) Open circles (O) indicate data for trichloromethylmercurials CCl_3HgR with R groups as indicated: A, CCl_3; B, C_6H_5; C, Cl; D, Br; E, Cl + $CH_3O(CH_2CH_2O)_2CH_3$ coordinated to Hg. Closed circles (•) indicate data for organic trichloromethanes CCl_3R with R groups as indicated: F, H; G, CH_3; H, $CH(OH)_2$; I, CH(OH) (NH_2); J, CCl_3; K, cyclo-$C_4Cl_2(CCl_3)$; L, cyclo-$C_8Cl_4(= CCl_2)_2$- (CCl_3); M, C_6H_4Cl-4, N, C_5Cl_5; P, CH(OH) (OC_2H_5); R, CH(OH) (OCH_3). Data are taken from References 1, 3, 4, and 5.

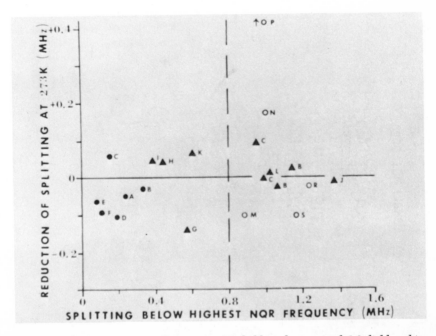

Figure 3. NQR frequency splittings for 2,6-dichlorophenoxy and 2,6-dichlorothio-phenoxy compounds at 77K compared with the reduction of these splittings at 273K. Closed circles (●) indicate data for nonmetal derivatives in which the chlorine is not being affected by hydrogen bonding; triangles (▲) indicate data for phenols and thiophenols with hydrogen bonding to the chlorine atom in question; and open circles (○) are for mercurials. Data points for $4\text{-}X\text{-}C_6H_2Cl_2\text{-}2,6\text{-}YR$ are as follows (symbol = X, Y, R); $A = H, O, CH_3$; $B = F, O, H$; $C = CN, O, H$; $D = NO_2, O, CH_3$; $E = F, O, CH_3$; $F = H, S, CH_3$; $G = H, O, H$; $H = CH_3, O, H$; $I = NH_2, O, H$; $J = Cl, O, H$; $K = I, O, H$; $L = CHO, O, H$; $M = H, O, HgC_6H_5$; $N = H, O, HgCH_2C_6H_5$; $P = H, O, HgC_6H_2\text{-}[CH(CH_3)_2]_3\text{-}2,4,6$; $R = H, O, HgC_6H_4N(CH_3)_2\text{-}4$; $S = H, S, HgC_6H_5$. Data taken from References 7, 8, 9, and 10 and this work (Table I).

intramolecular five-membered ring formation with one ortho chlorine. Substantial splittings of the NQR frequencies of the 2 and
6 chlorines also result from hydrogen bonding (11); these are not
consistently reduced in magnitude by raising the temperature.
This prediction should hold for an intramolecularly-interacting
chlorine regardless of whether it is interacting with hydrogen
or a metal.

The open circles of Fig. 3 (and Table 1) show the results to
date for the mercury derivatives of 2,6-dichlorophenol and the
thio analogue. The splittings range up to 1.2 MHz, so interactions are evidently present. Most, but not all, of these points
seem to be distributed about zero on the vertical axis, suggesting that the interaction is usually intramolecular. (There can,
of course, be intermolecular interactions in addition to, or in
place of, intramolecular interactions.) Crystal-structure work
has been done on two compounds very similar to those included
here, which shows the presence of intramolecular coordination
with mercury (12) and copper (13).

TABLE 1.   NQR FREQUENCIES OF MERCURY 2,6-DICHLOROPHENOXIDES
AT SELECTED TEMPERATURES

Substituent on Hg	ν, 77K[a]	ν, 195K	ν, 273K
Phenyl	34.925	34.682	34.476
	34.044	33.752	33.500
Benzyl	35.004	34.608	34.299
	33.995	33.708	33.472
4-Dimethylaminophenyl	34.892	34.495	34.159
	33.657	33.230	32.897
2,4,6-Tris(isopropyl)phenyl	35.244	34.991[b]	b
	34.147	34.014[b]	b

a. Frequencies, in MHz, at temperature indicated.   77K spectra
were first reported in ref. 7.
b. Signals not detected at 195K or higher.   Frequency listed was
obtained at 110K.

Time does not allow us to go through the other cases in
detail. To summarize our results, however, the pentachlorophenyl-
mercurials (Figure 1), which might form 4-membered planar rings
through intramolecular interaction, seem to do so. By way of
contrast, the pentachlorocyclopentadienylmercurials could form a
3-membered ring via their allylic chlorine, and 4-membered non-
planar rings via two vinylic chlorines. From the NQR evidence,
interactions with mercury occur with both types of chlorine (1),
but in both cases these are intermolecular. Hence, the NQR evidence to date suggests that, for an intramolecular chlorine-
mercury interaction to occur, there must be a five-membered or a
planar four-membered ring formed. These rings, indeed, are the
more favorable ones for overlap of the chlorine lone-pair electrons with vacant metal orbitals. The results, however, do not
exclude an electrostatic interpretation of the interaction.

In order to probe this matter further, we are preparing the chlorophenoxides of a number of other metals and studying them by NQR and by other spectroscopic methods. Some metals we are choosing for their propensity to engage in ionic bonding only; others we are selecting for their reputation for having vacant orbitals available for covalent bonding. Some should be "hard", and others "soft". To date we have some preliminary results: the Tl^+, Na^+, and K^+ chlorophenoxides studied so far show no significant (>0.8 MHz) splitting of the 2 and 6 chlorine NQR signals, while the copper (II) chlorophenoxides show quite large splittings (up to 2 MHz). Any predictions as to which metal might have the most promise in promoting the degradation of waste chlorocarbons must, however, await considerably more work.

We wish to thank the Research Corporation for a Cottrell College Science Grant in support of this work, and Maria Miscikowski, Wei Lan Wong, and Tim Bonner for their preliminary work on the derivatives of other metals.

Literature Cited

1. Wulfsberg, G., West, R., and Rao, V.N.M., _J. Organometal. Chem._, (1975) 86, 303.
2. Ingold, C.K., "Structure and Mechanism in Organic Chemistry," 2nd. ed., 479-83, Cornell University Press, Ithaca, 1969.
3. Biryukov, I.P., Voronkov, M.G., and Safin, I.A., "Tables of Nuclear Quadrupole Resonance Frequencies," Israel Program for Scientific Translations, Jerusalem, 1969.
4. Hashimoto, M., and Mano, K., _Bull. Chem. Soc. Jap._, (1972) 45, 706.
5. Kiichi, T., Nakamura, N., and Chihara, H., _J. Magn. Reson._, (1972) 6, 516.
6. Babushkina, T.A., Bryukhova, E.V., Velichko, F.K., Pakhomov, V.I., and Semin, G.K., _J. Struct. Chem._, (1968) 9, 153.
7. Kravtsov, D.N., Zhukov, A.P., Faingor, B.A., Rokhlina, El. M., Semin, G.K., and Nesmeyanov, G.K., _Bull. Acad. Sci. USSR, Div. Chem. Sci._, (1968) 1611.
8. Kravtsov, D.N., Zhukov, A.P., Babushkina, T.A., Bryukhova, T.A., Golovchenko., L.S., and Semin, G.K., _Bull. Acad. Sci. USSR, Div. Chem. Sci._, (1972) 1655.
9. Kravtsov, D.N., Semin, G.K., Zhukov, A.P., Babushkina, T.A., Rokhlina, E.M., and Nesmeyanov, A.N., _Theor.Exper.Chem._, (1972) 9, 401.
10. Pies, W., and Weiss, _Advances in Nucl. Quad. Resonance_, (1974) 1, 57.
11. Baker, A.W., and Kaeding, W.W., _J. Am. Chem. Soc._, (1959) 81, 5904.
12. Kuz'mina, L.G., Bokii, N.G., Struchkov, Yu. T., Kravtsov, D. N., and Golovchenko, L.S., _J. Struct. Chem._, (1973) 14, 463.
13. Wong, R.Y., Palmer, K.J., and Tomimatsu, Y., _Acta Cryst. Sec. B_, (1976) B32, 567.

APRIL 5, 1978